Camelot

MUSIC BY
FREDERICK LOEWE

BOOK AND LYRICS BY
ALAN JAY LERNER

CAMELOT

Music by
FREDERICK LOEWE

Book and Lyrics by
ALAN JAY LERNER

Based on
The Once and Future King
by T. H. WHITE

Vocal Score

Edited by FRANZ ALLERS
Piano Reduction by TRUDE RITTMAN

International Music Publications Limited
Griffin House 161 Hammersmith Road London W6 8BS England

CAMELOT

Produced by the Messrs. LERNER • LOEWE • HART
December 3, 1960 at the Majestic Theatre, New York City

Presented by JACK HYLTON
August 19, 1964 at the Theatre Royal, Drury Lane, London
Directed and Choreographed by
ROBERT HELPMANN
Scenery and Costumes Designed by JOHN TRUSCOTT
Lighting by RICHARD PILBROW
Musical Direction by KENNETH ALWYN
Orchestrations by ROBERT RUSSELL BENNETT and PHILIP J. LANG

Cast of Characters
(*In order of appearance*)

SIR DINADAN	Victor Flattery
SIR CLARIUS	Paul Ferris
SIR LIONEL	Raymond Edwards
SIR SAGRAMORE	Brian Hewitt Jones
MERLYN	Miles Malleson
ARTHUR	Laurence Harvey
GUENEVERE	Elizabeth Larner
LADY ANNE	Maryetta Midgeley
LADY SYBIL	Elaine Hewitt
NIMUE	Josephine Gordon
LANCELOT	Barry Kent
SQUIRE DAP	John Scarborough
PELLINORE	Cardew Robinson
ARCHBISHOP	John Scarborough
MORDRED	Nicky Henson
MORGAN LE FEY	Moyra Fraser
TOM	Kit Williams

PAGES: Kevin Crowhurst, Frank Knight.

LORDS AND LADIES OF CAMELOT: John Bannon, Diana Beall, Theresia Bester, Diana Bradney, Yvonne Chaplin, Ann Chivers, James Christiansen, John Clifford, Joyanne Delancey, Gillian Elvins, Joyce Endean, Penny Everton, Robert Ivan Foster, Norman Furber, Caroline Haig, Richard Hazell, Lewis Henry, Robert Howe, Peter Johnston, Michael Jones, Tony Kemp, Lynn Leishman, Jill Longstaffe, Jean Mostyn, Margaret McQueen, George Nichol, Alan Page, Bryan Payne, Jeanette Roach, Bernard Sharpe, Robin Sherringham, Anthea Slatter, Lorraine Smith, Wallace Stephenson, Gordon Traynor, Heather Walford, Tom Walling, John Walsh, Jane Walter, Jennie Walton, Annabella Weston, Ralph Wood, Felicity Wright, Gordon Yeats.

HERALDS: Bryan Payne, John Clifford.

JOUSTING MARSHALS: John Bannon, Alan Page.

FRENCH KNIGHTS: Peter Johnston, George Nichol, John Walsh, Gordon Yeats.

SCOTS KNIGHTS: John Clifford, James Christiansen, Lewis Henry, Alan Page, Wallace Stephenson, Gordon Traynor.

EXECUTIONER: Robin Sherringham.

NUNS: Theresia Bester, Yvonne Chaplin, Jill Longstaffe, Lorraine Smith, Margaret McQueen, Jeanette Roach, Heather Walford, Annabella Weston.

CAMELOT

Synopsis of Scenes

ACT I

ACT II

Musical Programme

ACT I

ACT II

CAMELOT
Overture

No. 1

FREDERICK LOEWE

B Poco meno mosso

C

D

Moderato, con espressione

Chappell

Ped. each beat

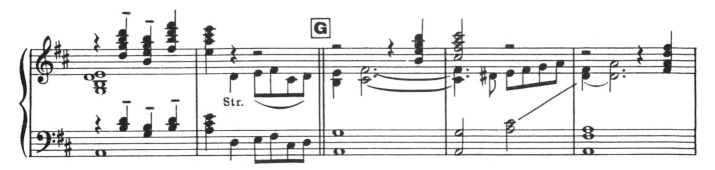

Chappell

12

47520
Chappell

No. 2   March

Cue: SIR DINADIN: We will meet Lady Guenevere at the foot of the hill in traditional fashion

Dialogue

Chappell

No.3 I Wonder What The King Is Doing Tonight

ALAN JAY LERNER

FREDERICK LOEWE

Cue: ARTHUR: ... That's precisely what you are doing. Every last blessed one of you.

Chappell

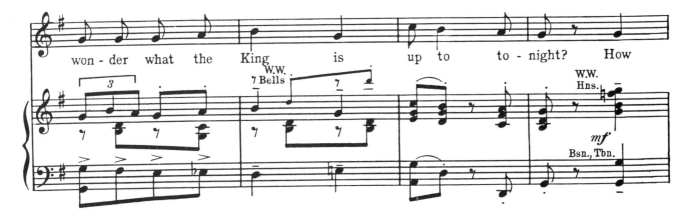

won - der what the King is up to to - night? How

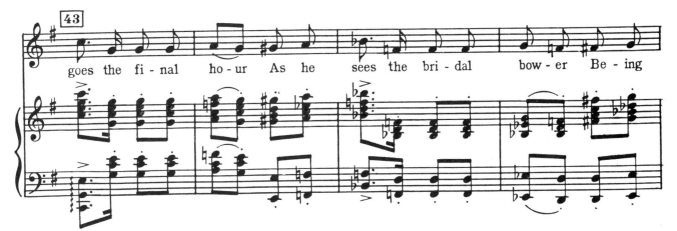

goes the fi - nal ho - ur As he sees the bri - dal bow - er Be - ing

le - gal - ly and re - gal - ly pre - pared? Well, I'll

tell you what the King is do - ing to - night: He's

Chappell

18

scared!　　　　　　　　　　　　He's　scared!

You　mean　that　a　King　who　fought　a　drag - on,

Whacked him in two and　fixed his wag - on,　Goes　to　be　wed　in　ter - ror　and　dis-

tress?　　　　　　　　　　　　Yes!　　　　　　　　　　　　A

Chappell

71 war - ri - or who's so calm in bat - tle, E - ven his ar - mor

Xyl.

p W.W., Str.

does - n't rat - tle, Fac - es a wom - an pet - ri - fied with

77 fright? Right! You

+Hns.

+Tbn.

81 mean that ap - pal - ling clam - our - ing That sounds like a black - smith

+Xyl.
Hp.

W.W.
Hns.
Tpts. *pp*

f

pp

Chappell

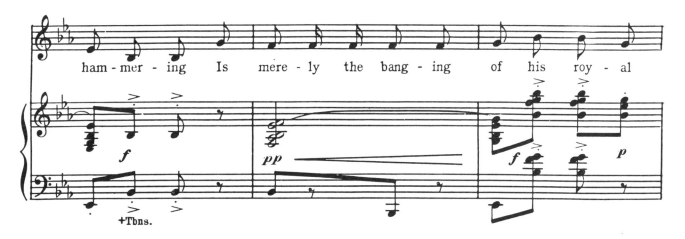

ham - mer - ing Is mere - ly the bang - ing of his roy - al

knees? Please! You

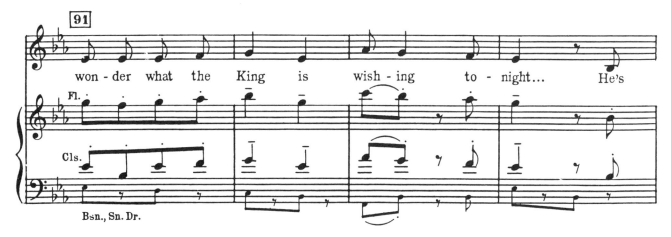

won - der what the King is wish - ing to - night... He's

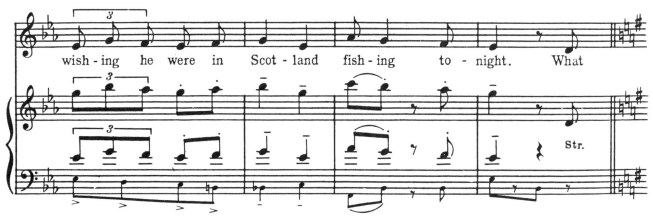

wish - ing he were in Scot - land fish - ing to - night. What

oc - cu - pies his time while wait - ing for the bride? He's

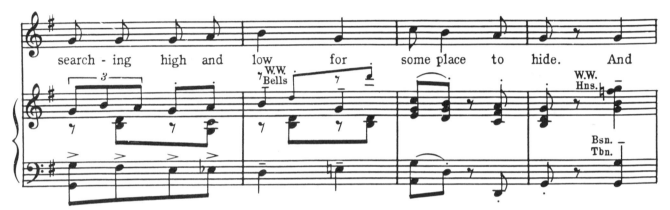

search - ing high and low for some place to hide. And

oh, the ex - pec - ta - tion, The sub - lime an - tic - i - pa - tion He must

feel a - bout the wed - ding night to come! Well! I'll

Chappell

22

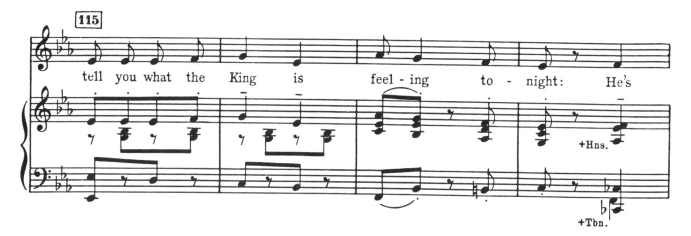

47520

Chappell

No. 4   The Simple Joys Of Maidenhood

GUENEVERE comes running on, as if being pursued.

Copyright © 1960 (unpub.) & 1961 by Alan Jay Lerner and Frederick Loewe

C

32 Allegro
(with vehement rebellion)

won't o - bey you an - y - more! You've gone a bit too far. I

won't be bid and bar - gain'd for Like beads at a ba - zaar. St.

40

Gen - e - vieve, I've run a - way, E - lud - ed them and fled, And from

now on I in - tend to pray to some - one else in - stead.

Chappell

F
87 Allegretto
(She sings)

Where are the sim-ple joys of maid-en-hood?___ Where are

Lute colla voce

pp Str.

all those a-dor-ing, dar-ing boys?_____ Where's the

Hp. Vc.

95

knight pin-ing so for me He leaps to death in woe for me? Oh,

where are a maid-en's sim-ple joys?_____ Shan't

Cls.

Vc.

+Bsn.

Chappell

I have the nor-mal life a maid-en should?_____ Shall I

nev-er be res-cued in the wood?_____ Shall two

knights nev-er tilt for me And let their blood be spilt for me? Oh,

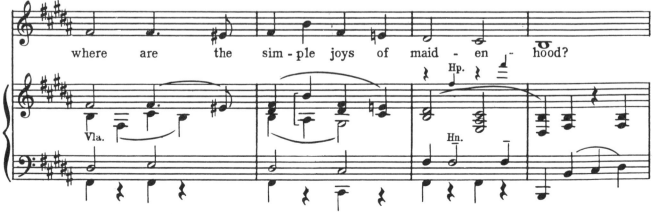

where are the sim-ple joys of maid-en-hood?

Chappell

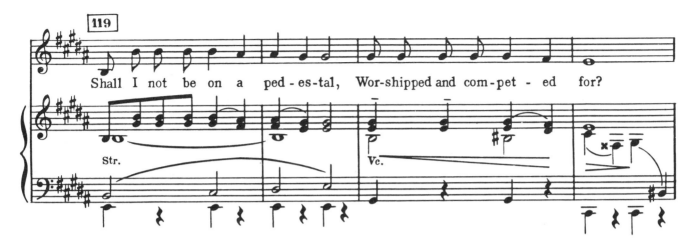

Shall I not be on a ped-es-tal, Wor-shipped and com-pet - ed for?

Not be car-ried off, or bet-ter st'll, Cause a lit-tle war?

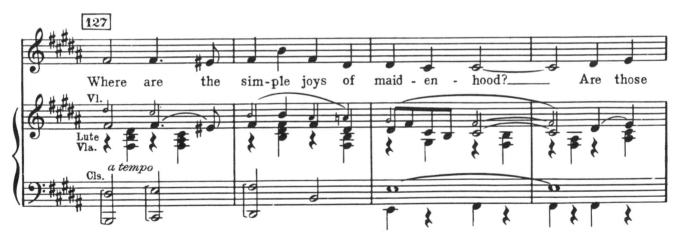

Where are the sim-ple joys of maid-en - hood?____ Are those

sweet, gen - tle pleas-ures gone for good?____ Shall a

Chappell

feud not be-gin for me? Shall kith not kill their kin for me? Oh,

where are the triv-ial joys...? Harm-less, con-viv-ial joys..?

Str., Gtr.

Hp.
Bells

Where are the sim-ple joys of maid - en -

poco rall.

Poco più mosso

(Dialogue)

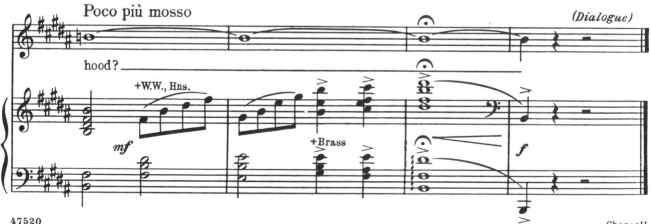

hood?_____

+W.W., Hns.

mf

+Brass

f

Chappell

No. 5

Camelot

Cue: ARTHUR: Ordained by decree!
...Extremely uncommon.
GUENEVERE: Oh, come now.

ARTHUR: It's true! It's true! The crown has made it clear:_ The cli-mate must be per-fect all the year._ A law was made a dis-tant moon a-go here,_ Ju-ly and Au-gust can-not be too hot; And

Copyright © 1960 by Alan Jay Lerner and Frederick Loewe

Chappell

there's a le - gal lim - it to the snow here ____ In

Ca - me - lot. The

win - ter is for - bid - den till De - cem - ber ____ And

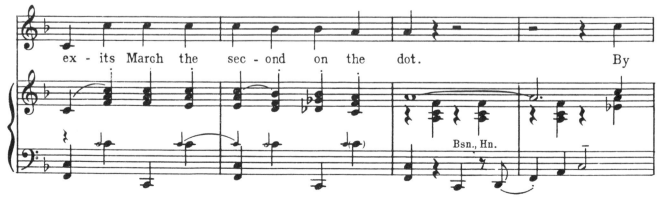

ex - its March the sec - ond on the dot. By

Chappell

or - der sum - mer ling - ers through Sep - tem - ber___ In

Ca - me - lot.

Ca - me - lot! Ca - me - lot! I know it

sounds a bit bi - zarre. But in

Chappell

Ca - me - lot,   Ca - me - lot,   That's

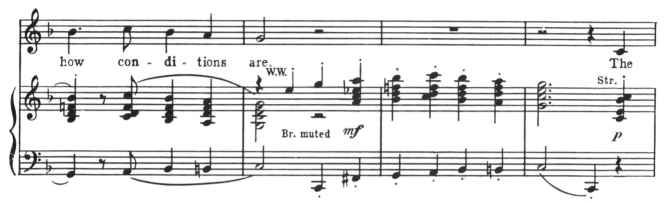

how con - di - tions are.   The

rain may nev - er fall till aft - er sun - down._____ By

eight the morn - ing fog must dis - ap - pear._____ In

Chappell

short, there's sim - ply not   A more con - gen - ial   spot   For

Poco meno mosso

happ' - ly - ev - er - - - aft - er - ing   than   here   In

Tempo giusto

Ca - - me - - lot.

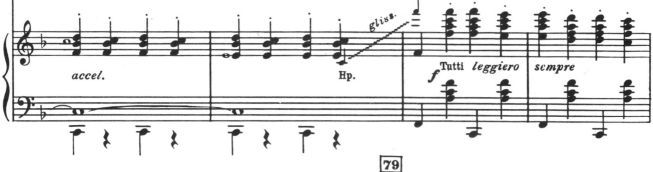

GUENEVERE: And   I   suppose

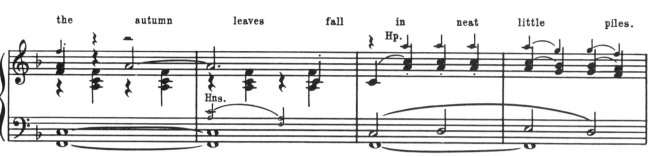

the autumn leaves fall in neat little piles.

ARTHUR: Oh, no, Milady, they **87** blow away completely.

At night, of course. GUENEVERE: Of course!

He moves closer to her. **95**

Ca - me - lot!

Ca - me - lot! I know it gives a per - son pause,

 Chappell

But in Ca - me - lot,

Ca - me - lot, Those are the le - gal laws.

The snow may nev — er slush up - on the

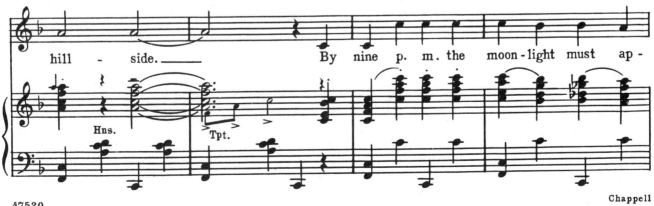

hill - side. By nine p. m. the moon - light must ap -

pear. _____ In short, there's sim - ply not A

more con - gen - ial spot For happ' - ly - ev - er - aft - er - ing than

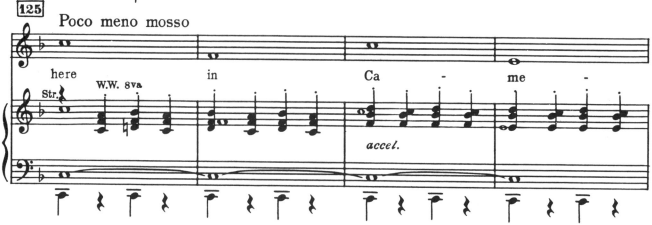

125 Poco meno mosso

here in Ca - me -

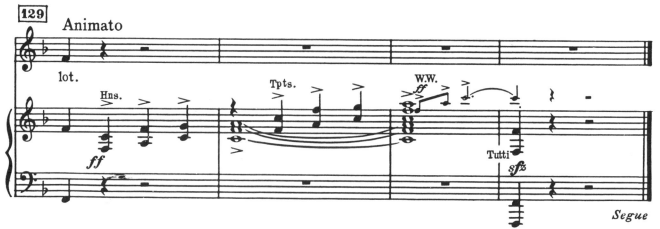

129 Animato

lot.

Segue

Chappell

No. 6

Guenevere's Welcome

Cue: SIR DINADAN: There she is!
GUENEVERE: Wart, please....

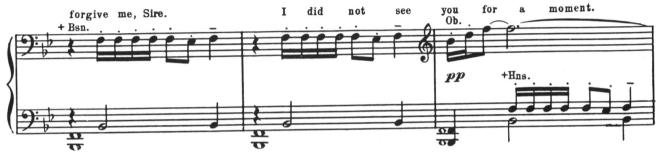

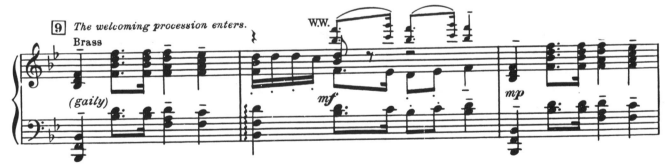

Chappell

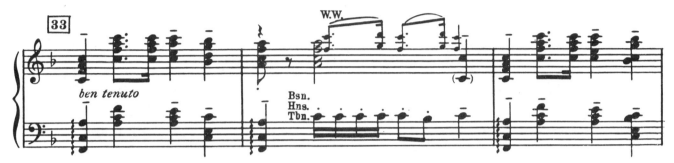

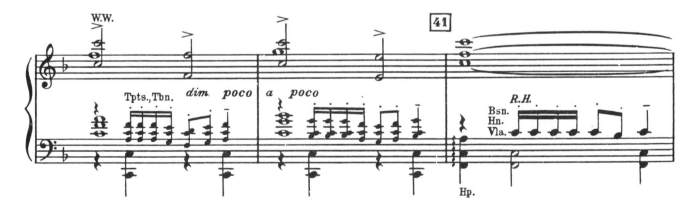

No.7   End of Scene (Camelot Reprise)

Cue: ARTHUR:... And since I am, I have been ill at ease in my crown. Until I dropped from the tree and my eyes beheld you.

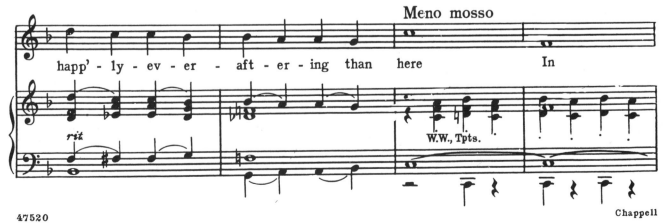

Chappell

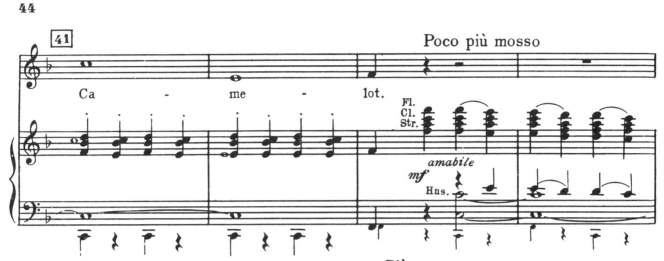

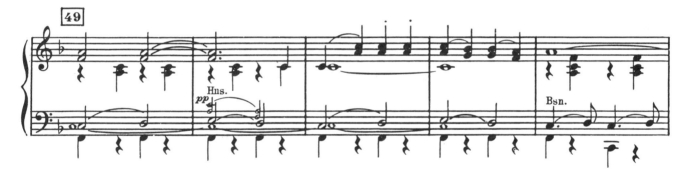

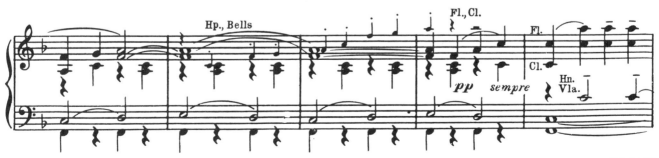

Chappell

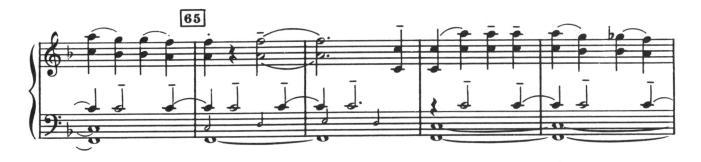

Chappell

Follow Me

Cue: MERLYN:...One year... two years...what does it matter? I can see a night five years from now...

Copyright © 1960 by Alan Jay Lerner and Frederick Loewe

Chappell

Chappell

48

Chappell

No.9 End Of Antechamber Scene

Cue: **GUENEVERE:** It's marvellous.

ARTHUR: Yes, it is. It's marvellous. Absolutely marvellous. Page, give the signal.

PAGE: Yes, your Majesty.

Chappell

No. 10   *Countryside near Camelot.*   C'est Moi

Copyright © 1960 (unpub.) & 1962 by Alan Jay Lerner and Frederick Loewe   Chappell

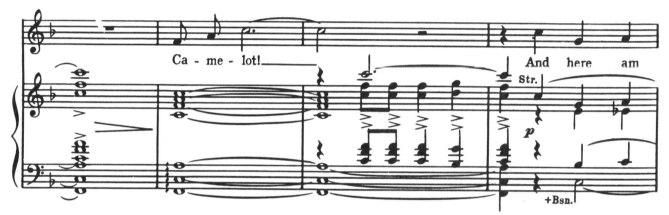

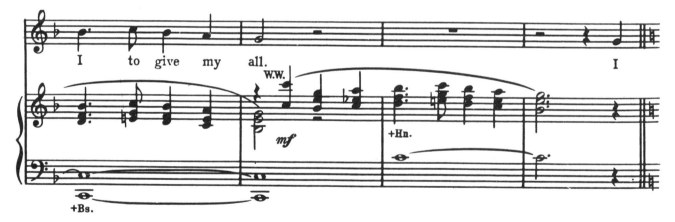

all that and more I shall be! _____ A

33 Alla marcia

knight of the ta - ble round should be in - vin - ci - ble;   Suc-
soul of a knight should be a thing re - mark - a - ble: His

ceed where a less fan - tas - tic man would fail; _____   Climb a
heart and his mind as pure as morn - ing dew. _____   With a

41

wall no one else can climb; Cleave a drag - on in rec - ord time; Swim a
will and a self - re - straint That's the en - vy of ev - 'ry saint,   He could

Chappell

moat in a coat of heav-y i-ron mail._____ No
eas-i-ly work a mir-a-cle or two!_____ To

mat-ter the pain he ought to be un-winc-a-ble, Im-
love and de-sire he ought to be un-spark-a-ble. The

poss-i-ble deeds should be his dai-ly fare. But
ways of the flesh should of-fer no al-lure. But

where in the world Is there in the world A
where in the world Is there in the world A

Chappell

man _ so extra - or - di - naire? _____
man _ so un touch'd and pure? _____

W.W. Str. *en dehors*

Bsn.,Hn.,Vc.

67 **Allegretto scherzando**

/(Spoken modestly) C'est moi...C'est

C'est moi! C'est moi, I'm forced to ad - mit! 'Tis
moi! C'est moi, I blush to dis - close, I'm

W.W.,Str.,Hp.

p

I, I hum - bly re - ply. _____ That mor - tal who These
far too no - ble to lie. _____ That man in whom These

mar - vels can do, C'est moi, C'est moi, 'tis I! _____ I've
qual - i - ties bloom, C'est moi, C'est moi, 'tis I! _____ I've

Fl.,Cl.

mp

/2nd stanza only

nev - er lost In bat - tle or game. I'm
nev - er stray'd From all I be - lieve. I'm

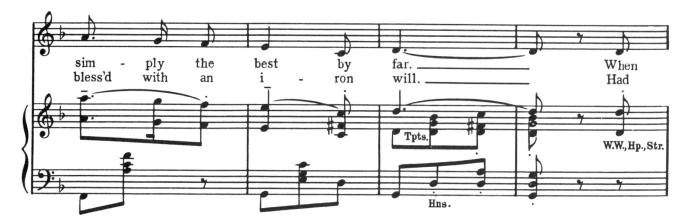

sim - ply the best by far. _____ When
bless'd with an i - ron will. _____ Had

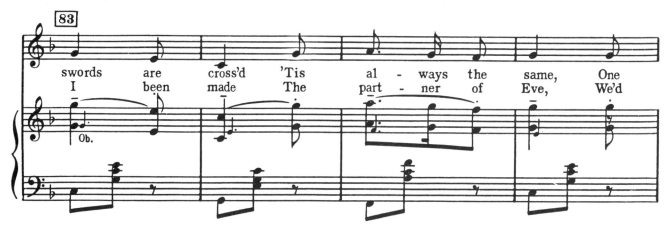

swords are cross'd 'Tis al - ways the same, One
I been made The part - ner of Eve, We'd

blow and au re - voir! _____ C'est
be in E - den still. _____ C'est

moi! C'est moi, So ad - mir - 'bly fit; A
moi! C'est moi, The an - gels have chose To

mf Hns., Str. div.

W.W.

French Pro - me - theus un - bound. _____ And here I stand with
fight their bat - tles be - low. _____ And here I stand as

Tbns.
Timp.

val - or un - told, Ex - cept - ion - 'ly brave, a - maz - ing - ly bold, To
pure as a pray'r, In - cred - i - bly clean, with vir - tue to spare, The

*)

serve at the Ta - ble Round! The
god - li - est man I know! C'est moi!

+Tbns.

ff Tutti   ff Tutti

Dialogue

*) Bars 97 and 98 are rit. in the 2nd stanza.
47520

Chappell

No. 11

The Lusty Month Of May
(Dance And Song)

Cue: ARTHUR:... Welcome, Lancelot. Bless you for coming, and welcome to the table. *(The scene changes.)*

Copyright © 1960 (unpub.) & 1961 by Alan Jay Lerner and Frederick Loewe

Chappell

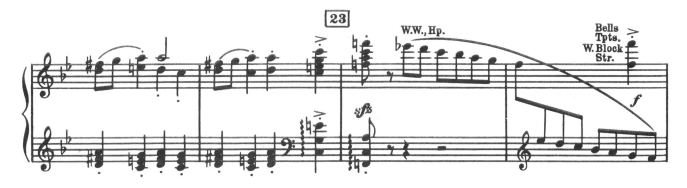

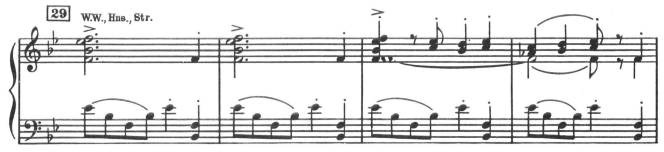

Chappell

Chappell

It's May, it's May, When love has it's way, It's May, A

gay ho - li - day.

Chappell

151

GUENEVERE

La la! It's

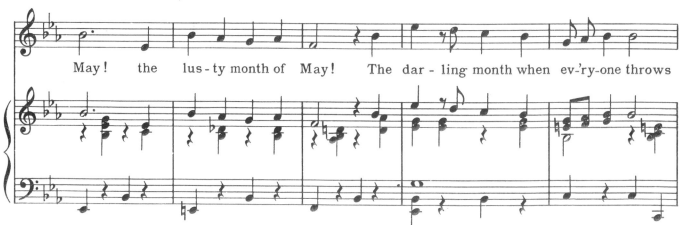

May! the lus-ty month of May! The dar-ling month when ev'ry-one throws

Chappell

self con-trol a - way! It's time to do a wretch-ed thing or

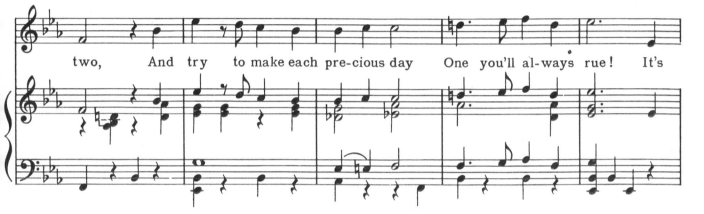

two, And try to make each pre-cious day One you'll al-ways rue! It's

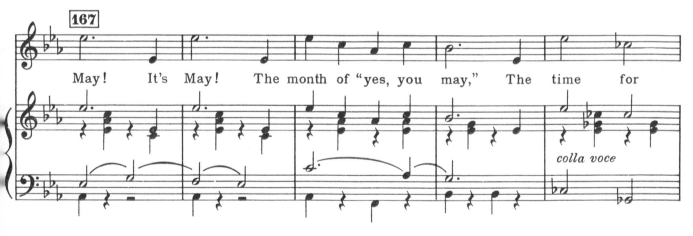

May! It's May! The month of "yes, you may," The time for

colla voce

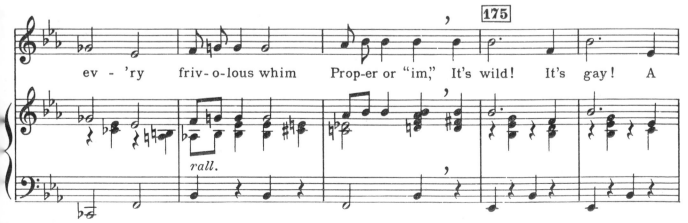

ev - 'ry friv-o-lous whim Prop-er or "im," It's wild! It's gay! A

rall.

Chappell

blot in ev-'ry way. The birds and bees with all of their vast

184

Am-or-ous past Gaze at the hu-man race a-ghast. The lus - -

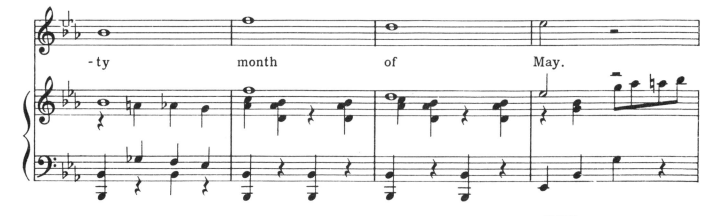

-ty month of May.

192

ENSEMBLE (Unis.)

Tra - la! It's

Chappell

May! The lus - ty month of May! The love - ly month when

ev -'ry - one goes bliss - ful - ly a - stray Tra - la! It's

here! That shock - ing time of year! When tons of wick - ed

lit - tle thoughts Mer - ri - ly ap - pear___ It's May! It's

Chappell

66

May! The month of great dis - may When all the

world is brim-ming with fun, Whole-some or "un" It's

216

mad! It's gay! A li - bel-ous dis - play. Those

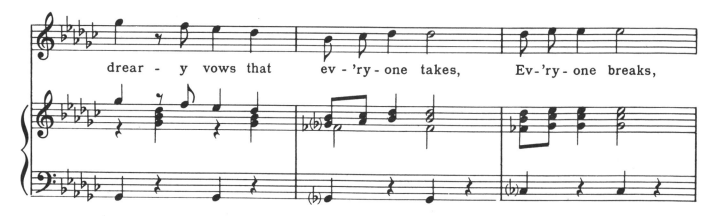

drear - y vows that ev - 'ry - one takes, Ev-'ry - one breaks,

47520

Chappell

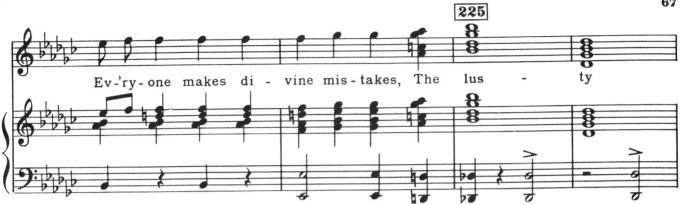

Ev-'ry-one makes di - vine mis-takes, The lus - ty

month of May.

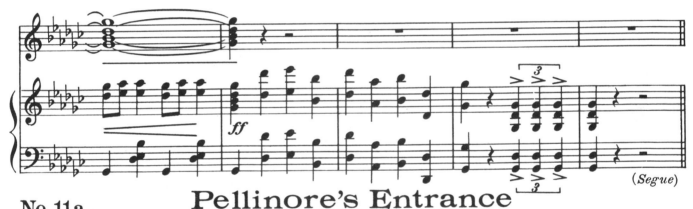

(Segue)

No. 11a Pellinore's Entrance

L'istesso tempo

(Dialogue)

Chappell

No. 12 Take Me To The Fair

Cue. GUENEVERE : Sir Lionel

SIR LIONEL : Your Majesty

Copyright © 1960 (unpub.) by Alan Jay Lerner and Frederick Loewe

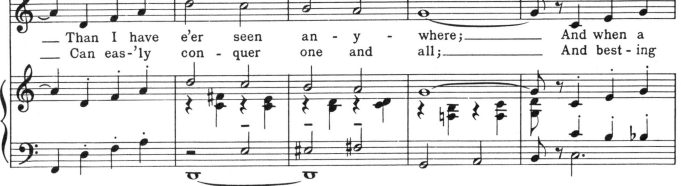

Lyrics:

who / know, I must in-vite in place of you, Some-one who / But it's tra-di-tion it should go To the un-

plain-ly is be-yond com-pare / ques-tion'd champ-ion in the hall;

The French-man's pow'r is more tre-men-dous / And I'm con-vinced that splen-did French-man

Than I have e'er seen an-y-where; And when a / Can eas-'ly con-quer one and all; And best-ing

Chappell

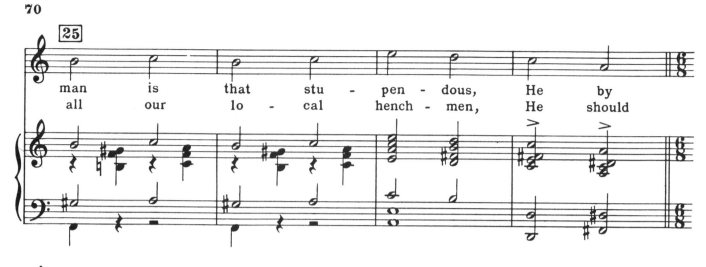

man is that stu - pen - dous, He by
all our lo - cal hench - men, He should

right should take me to the fair.
sit be - side me at the ball.

(LIONEL) Your ma - je - sty, let me tilt with him and
(SAGRAMORE) I beg of you, m'am, with - hold your in - vi -

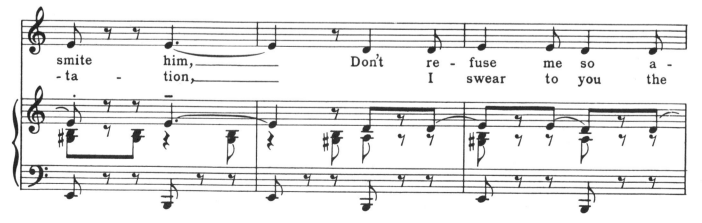

smite him, Don't re - fuse me so a -
-ta - tion, I swear to you the

Cappell

Chappell

His skull will crack! Well Then you may take me
He'll feel the draught! Well Then you may sit by

to the fair, _____ If you do all the
me at the ball. _____ If you de - mol - ish

things you prom - ise. _____ In fact my heart will
him in bat - tle. _____ In fact I know I'd

Chappell

break Should you not take me to_____
cry   Were   you not by   me at_____

67

the_____
the_____

fair._____
ball._____

1 GUENEVERE *(spoken)* SIR SAGRAMORE *(spoken)*
"Sir Sagramore" "Yes, Your Majesty" GUENEVERE *(sings)*

I have some

Fl. Clt. Vla.

rath - er pain - ful news Rel - a - tive to the sub - ject

who's To be be - side me at the next court

ball._____ You were the

2 **GUENEVERE** *(spoken)* **SIR DINADAN** *(spoken)*
"Sir Dinadan"   "My Lady"

GUENEVERE *(sings)*

Did - n't I prom - ise that you may Guide me to

Cha

London on the day That I go up to judge the

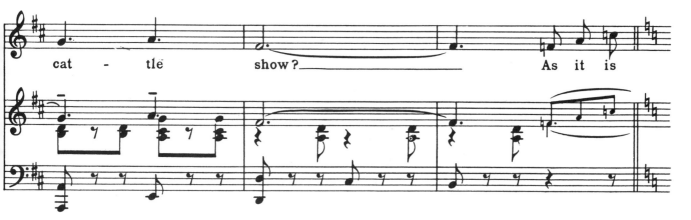

cat - tle show? As it is

89

quite a nast - y ride, There must be some - one at my

side Who'll be de - fend - ing me _____ from beast and foe. _____

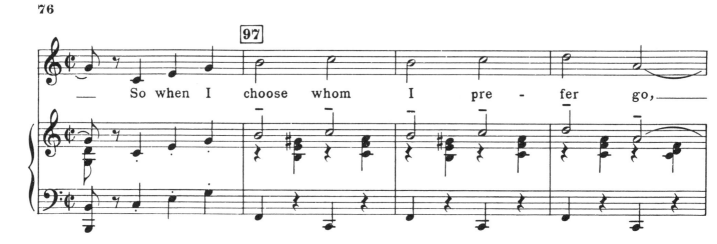

So when I choose whom I pre - fer go,

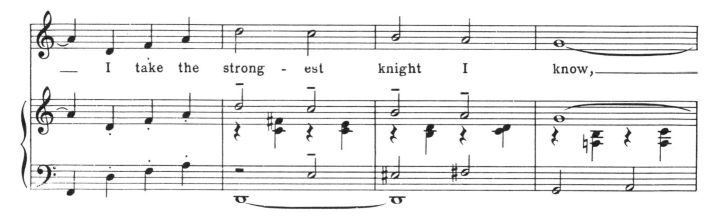

I take the strong - est knight I know,

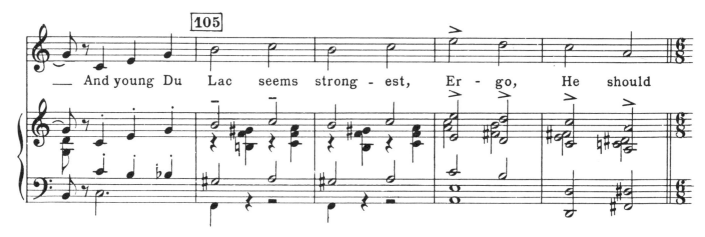

And young Du Lac seems strong - est, Er - go, He should

take me to the cat - tle show.

DINADAN

Your

maj - es - ty can't be - lieve this blus - t'ring prat - tle! _____

Let him prove it with a sword or lance in -

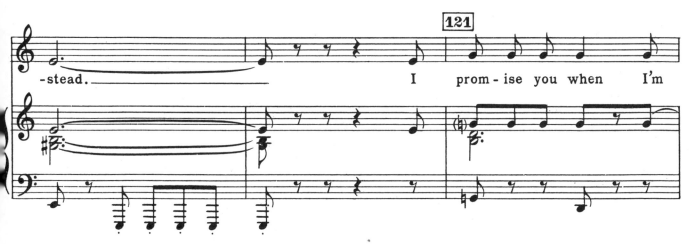

-stead. _____ I prom - ise you when I'm

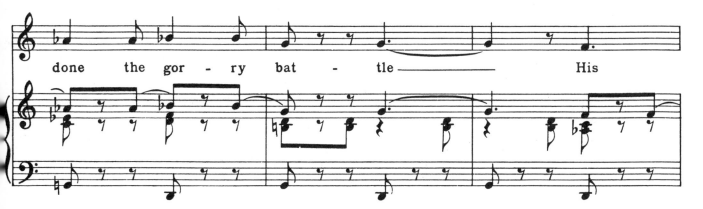

done the gor - ry bat - tle _____ His

Chappell

shoul-ders will be lone-some for his head!

128 *(spoken)* I'll vivisect him!

I'll sub-divide him! GUENEVERE *(spoken)* **129** Oh dear, dear, dear, dear, *(sings)* Dear! There you may guide me

In tempo

to the Show_____ If you can car - ry out your

139

pro - gramme.__ In fact I'd grieve in - side Should you not

Chappell

KNIGHTS: (Unis.)

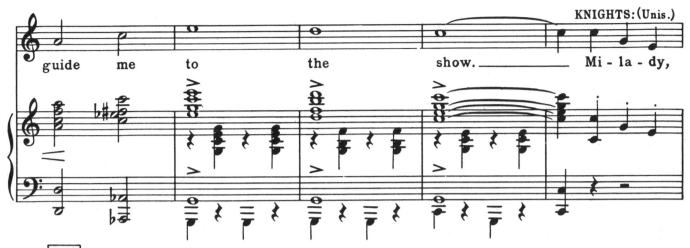

guide me to the show. _____ Mi - la - dy,

147

we shall put an end to _____ That Gal - lic bag of

155

noise and nerve, _____ When we do all that we in -

- tend to, _____ He'll be a plate of French *Hors D'oueures!* _____

Chappell

GUENEVERE 163

I do ap-plaud your no-ble goals,

Now let us see if you a - chieve them,

171

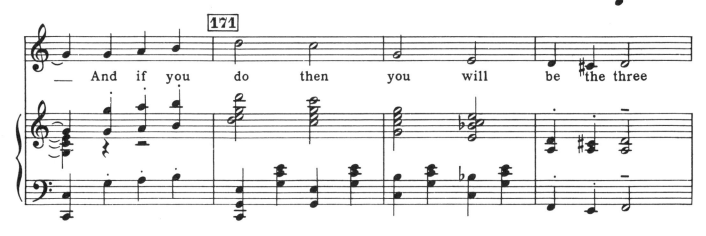

And if you do then you will be the three

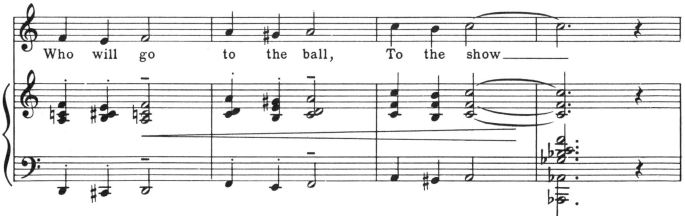

Who will go to the ball, To the show

 Chappell

Chappell

No. 13 Change of Scene- 5-6

Chappell

How To Handle A Woman

Cue: GUENEVERE:... let him command me! And Yours Humbly will graciously obey. What? What? *(She exits)*

ARTHUR: What?

        Blast!

        Blast you, Merlyn!

        This is all your fault!

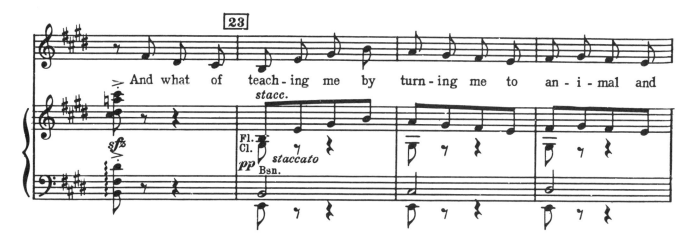

And what of teach-ing me by turn-ing me to an-i-mal and

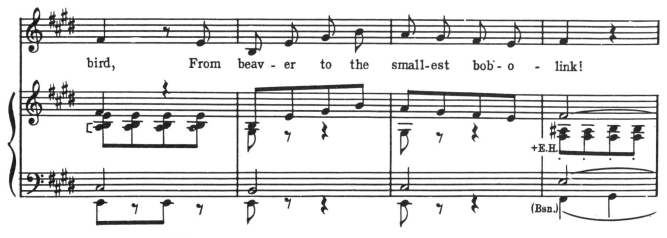

bird, From beav - er to the small-est bob-o - link!

I should have had a whirl At chang-ing to a girl, To

Chappell

learn the way the crea - tures think!

But

45 Tranquillo

was - n't there a night, on a sum-mer long gone by, We pass'd a cou-ple wran-gling a-

49

way;— And did I not say, Mer-lyn: What if that chap were I? And

Chappell

did he not give coun-cil and say..... What was it now? My mind's a

wall.___ Oh, yes! By jove, now I re - call.___

57 **Moderato**

How to han-dle a wom - an? There's a way, said the wise old

man; A way known by ev - 'ry wom-an Since the

whole rig-'ma-role be - gan. Do I flat-ter her? I begged him

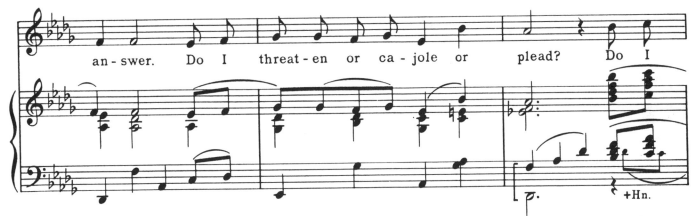

an-swer. Do I threat-en or ca-jole or plead? Do I

brood or play the gay ro-manc-er? Said he, smil-ing: No in -

- deed. How to han-dle a wom-an? Mark me

Chappell

well, I will tell you, Sir: The way to han-dle a

wom-an Is to love her... simp-ly

love her... Mere-ly love her...

love her... love her.

87
ponders a moment, then says: What's wrong, Jenny? Where are you these days? What are you
Hns.
Str.
Hp.
pp
thinking? I don't understand you. But no matter. Merlyn told me once: Never be too
Hp.
95
disturbed if you don't understand what a woman is thinking.
+E.H., Gtr.
Hp.
Str.
They don't do it often. But what do you do when they are
+Cl.
103
doing it? (He sings)
How to han - dle a wom - an? Mark me
Fl.
Str.
Tbns.
Hns., Hp.
(Hn.I)

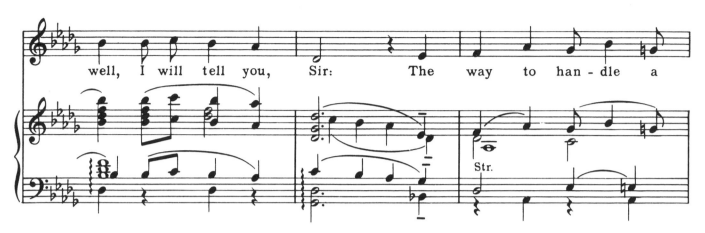

well, I will tell you, Sir: The way to han-dle a

109

wom-an Is to love her... sim-ply

love her Mere-ly love her___

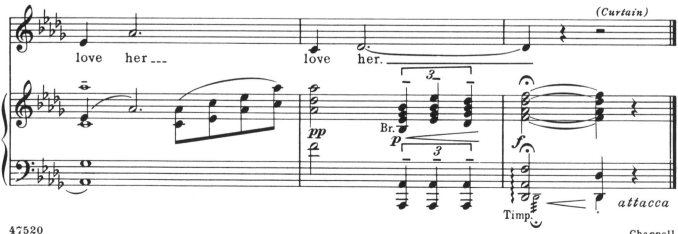

love her ___ love her. ___

(Curtain)

Chappell

Tent Scene

Piano

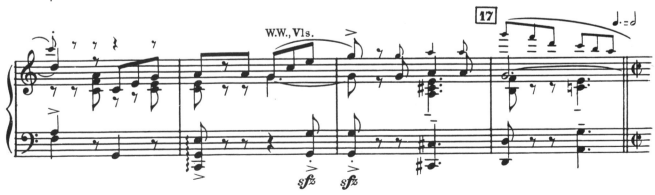

Chappell

The curtain rises. SIR LIONEL, SIR DINADAN, SIR SAGRAMORE with their squires, and

LANCELOT with DAP are preparing for the joust.

27

Hp.

31

LANCELOT: I wish you success, Milords.
(Dialogue) *(Dialogue continues)*

Chappell

The Tumblers

Cue: SIR LIONEL.... Then save your wishes for your continuing good health.

Chappell

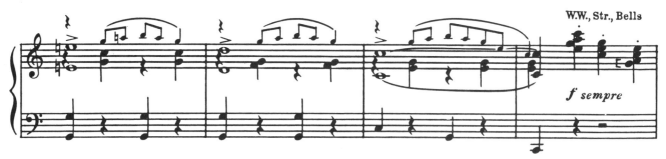

Chappell

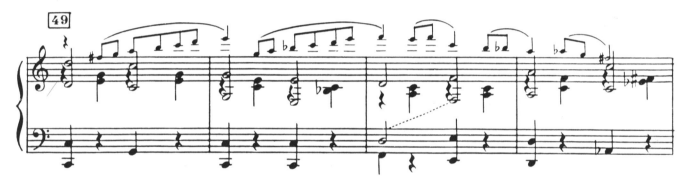

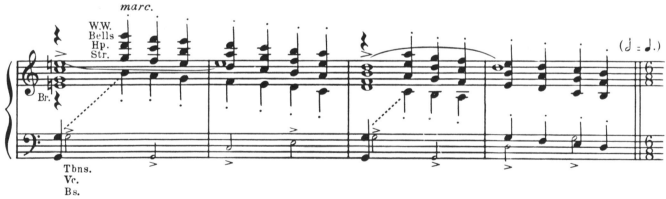

attacca

Chappell

No. 16a Entrance Of The Jousting Knights

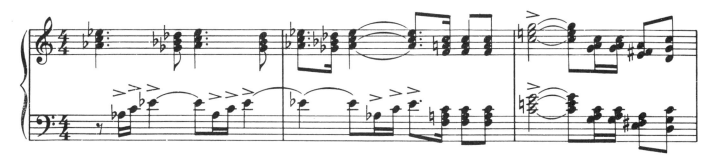

Chappell

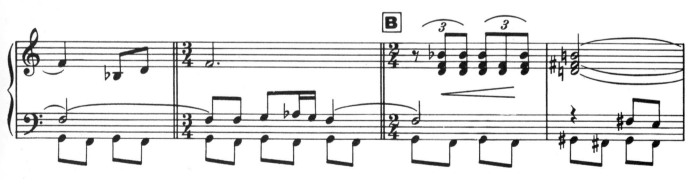

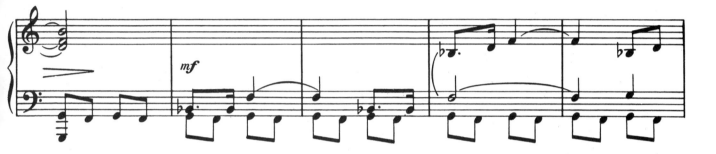

Chappell

Chappell

No. 17

The Jousts

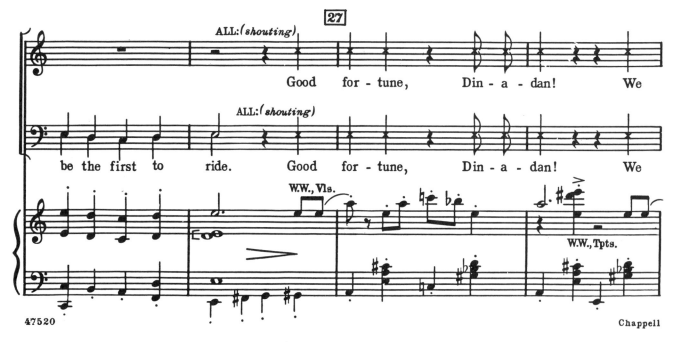

Chappell

Chappell

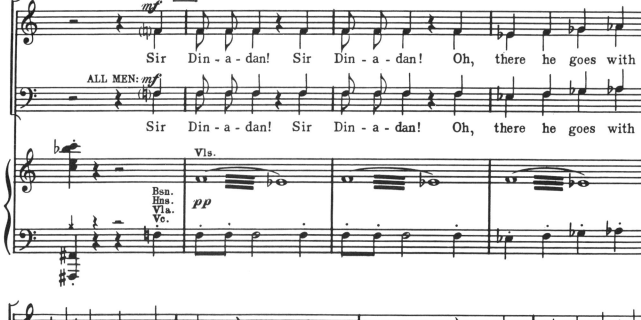

ALL WOMEN: *mf* **39**

Sir Din - a - dan! Sir Din - a - dan! Oh, there he goes with

ALL MEN: *mf*

Sir Din - a - dan! Sir Din - a - dan! Oh, there he goes with

Vls. *pp*

Bsn. / Hns. / Vla. / Vc.

all his might and main: He's got a stead-y

CLARIUS: There he goes! (ALL:)

all his might and main. He's got a stead-y

Eb Cl. Picc. *pp*

+Hp. / Dr., Bs.

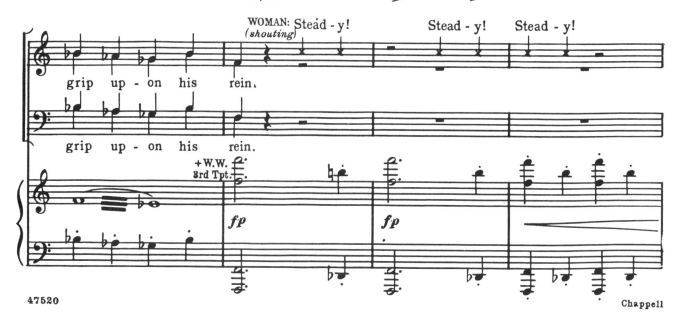

WOMAN: Stead - y! Stead - y! Stead - y!
(*shouting*)

grip up - on his rein.

grip up - on his rein.

+W.W. / 3rd Tpt.

fp *fp*

 Chappell

Chappell

104

47520

Chappell

85 Tempo Iº

93

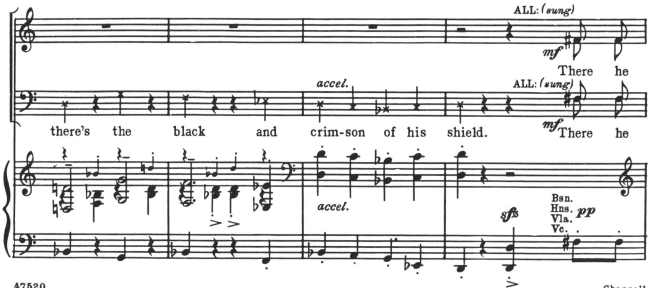

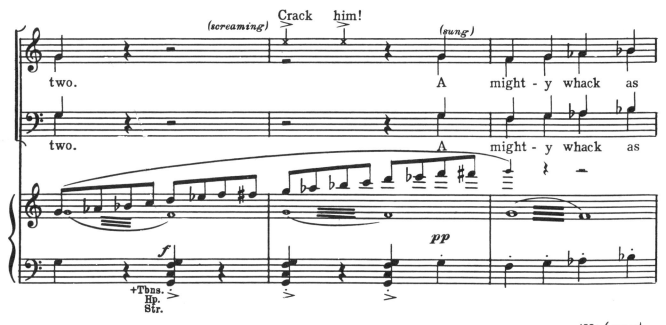

Chappell

Chappell

Chappell

Chappell

Chappell

Chappell

Chappell

118

Chappell

No. 18

Before I Gaze At You Again

Cue: ARTHUR: It might do you good to get away from Round Tables and chivalry for a little while. Don't you think?
(GUENEVERE does not answer)
Don't you think? *(She still doesn't answer. He turns and exits.)*

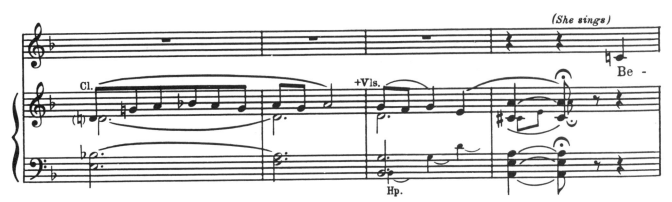

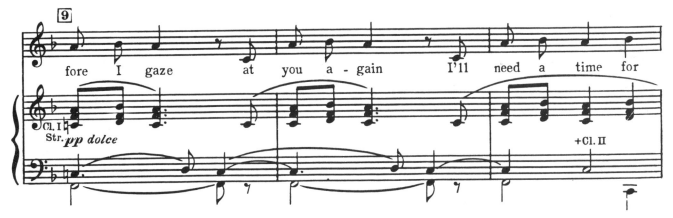

Copyright © 1960 (unpub.) & 1962 by Alan Jay Lerner and Frederick Loewe

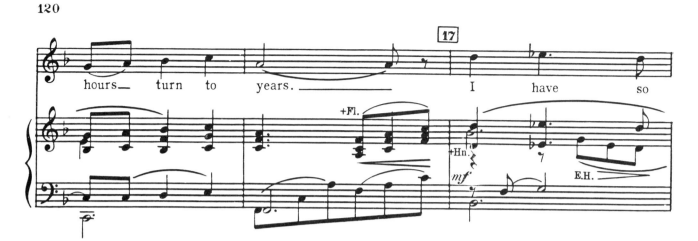

hours turn to years. I have so

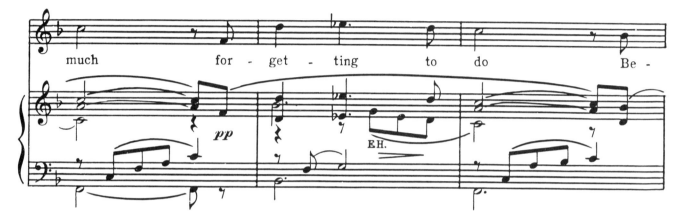

much for - get - ting to do Be -

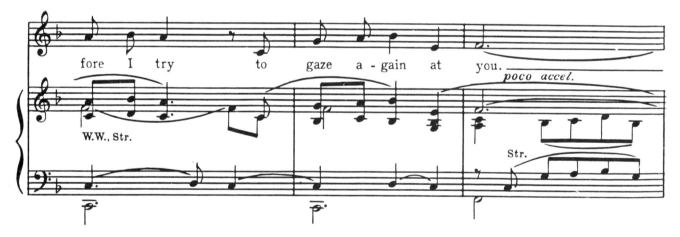

fore I try to gaze a - gain at you.

25 Poco più mosso

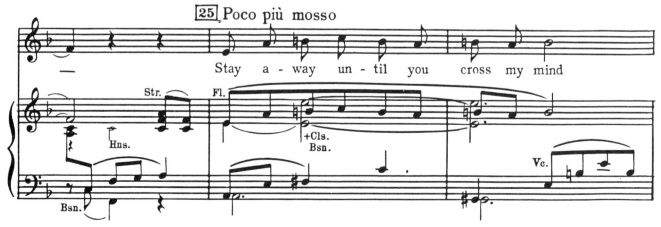

Stay a - way un - til you cross my mind

Chappell

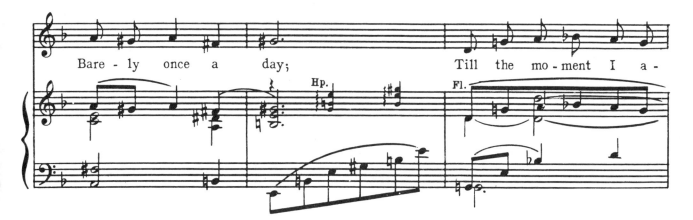

Bare - ly once a day; Till the mo - ment I a-

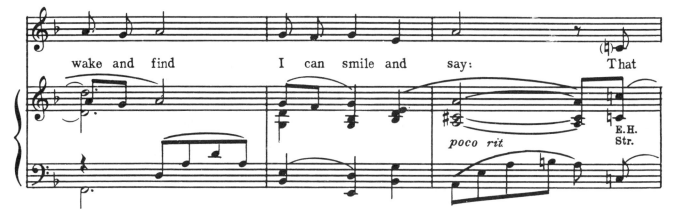

wake and find I can smile and say: That

33 Tempo Iº

I can gaze at you a - gain With - out a blush or

qualm, My eyes a - shine like new a - gain, My

Chappell

man - ner poised and calm. Stay far a - way, My

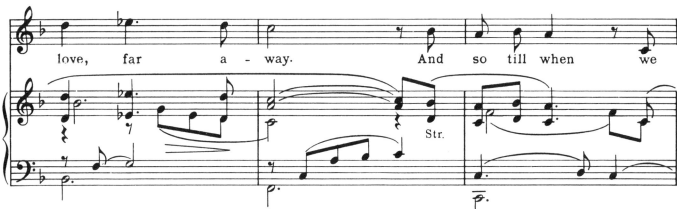

love, far a - way. And so till when we

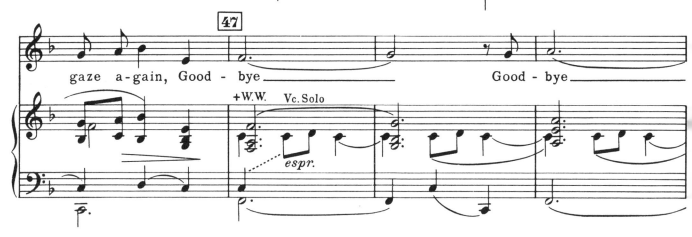

gaze a-gain, Good - bye _____ Good - bye _____

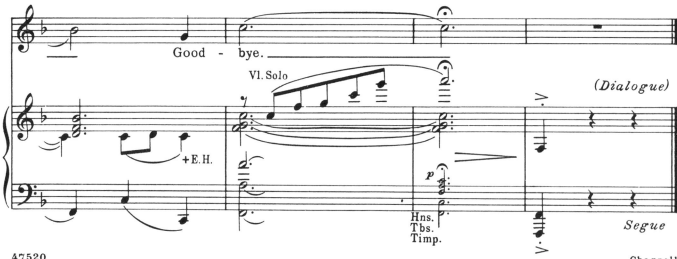

Good - bye. _____

(Dialogue)

Segue

Chappell

Cue: ARTHUR:... all borders will disappear...and all the things I dreamed... I dreamed... I dreamed.   *(Curtain)*
The scene changes.

The curtain rises on the Great Hall. Ladies and Gentlemen of

49 Con moto, moderato

the Court are filing in.

57

ARTHUR and GUENEVERE enter and take their places on the throne!

65 Maestoso

Chappell

ARTHUR: Excalibur!

75 Andante con moto

SIR DINADAN: To be invested Knights of the Round Table of England: of Brackley... Colgrevance.

(Colgrevance steps forward

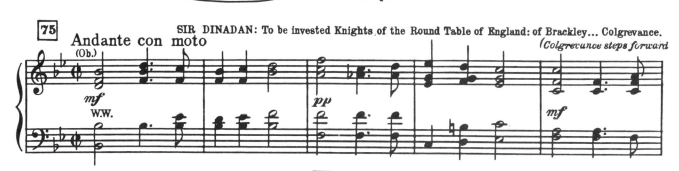

and is knighted.) Of Winchester... Bliant.   83   *(Bliant steps forward and is knighted.)* Of Wales... Guilliam.

(Guilliam steps forward and is knighted.) Of Cornwall,...Castor. *(Castor steps forward and is knighted.)*   91   Of Joyous Gard: Lancelot Du Lac.

(Lancelot steps forward. ARTHUR hesitates, then he knights Lancelot.)

Chappell

Chappell

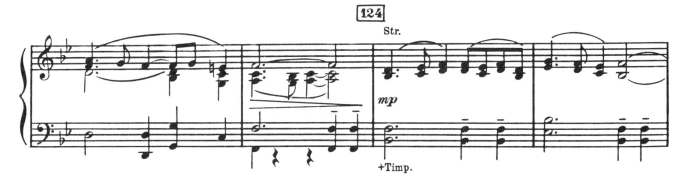

ARTHUR: *(alone in the Great Hall)*   Proposition: If I could choose, from every

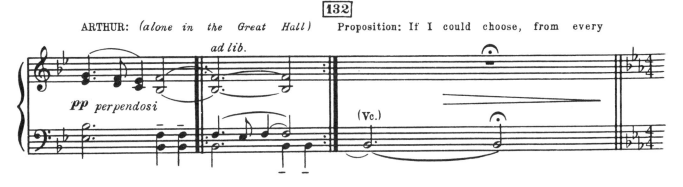

woman who breathes on this earth, the face I would most love, the smile, the touch, the voice, the heart, the laugh,

Molto tranquillo

Chappell

the soul itself, every detail and feature to the smallest strand of hair - they would all be Jenny's.

141 Proposition: If I could choose, from every man who breathes on this earth, a man for my brother

and a man for my son, a man for my friend, they would all be Lance.

149 Yes, I love them. I love them, and they answer me again with pain and torment. Be it sin or not sin, they betray

me in their hearts, and that's far sin enough. I see it in their eyes and feel it when they speak, and they must pay for

Chappell

it and be punished. I shan't be wounded and not return it in kind. I'm done with feeble hoping. I demand a man's vengeance.

161 Poco più grave

Proposition: I'm a King, not a man. And a civilized King. Could it

possibly be civilized to destroy what I love? Could it possibly be civilized to love myself above all?

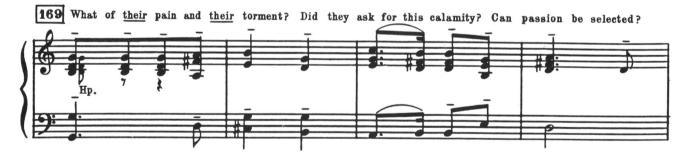

169 What of _their_ pain and _their_ torment? Did they ask for this calamity? Can passion be selected?

Is there any doubt of their devotion... to me, or to our Table?

Entr'acte

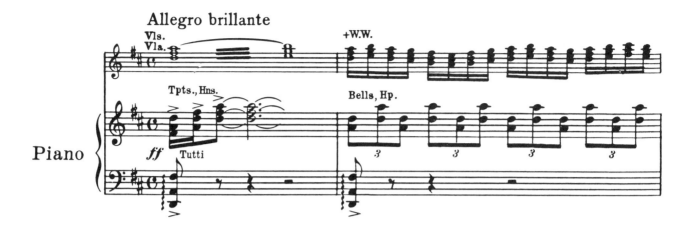

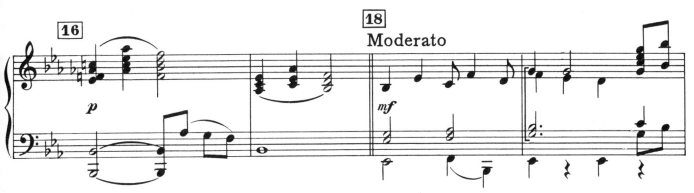

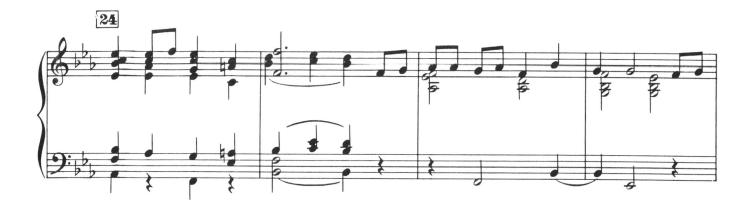

Chappell

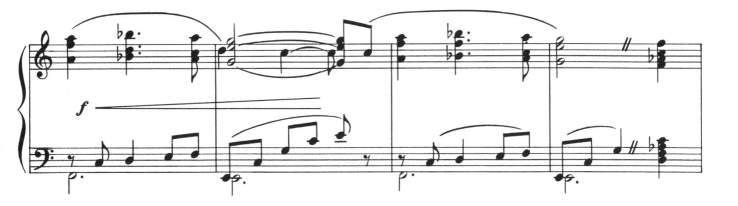

Chappell

Chappell

No. 21

Fie On Goodness
(MALE CHORUS)

Eight years of phil-an-throp-ic la - bour! _____ Der-ry down

dell! Gad, but it's hell! Oh, Fie on good-ness, Fie! _____

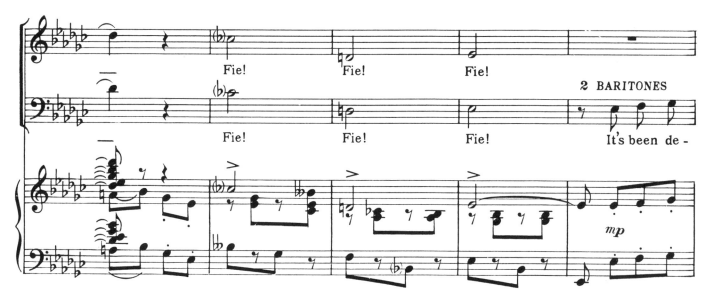

Fie! Fie! Fie!

2 BARITONES

Fie! Fie! Fie! It's been de-

Chappell

-press-ing all the way; Der-ry down, Der-ry down. And get-ting

3 BASSES

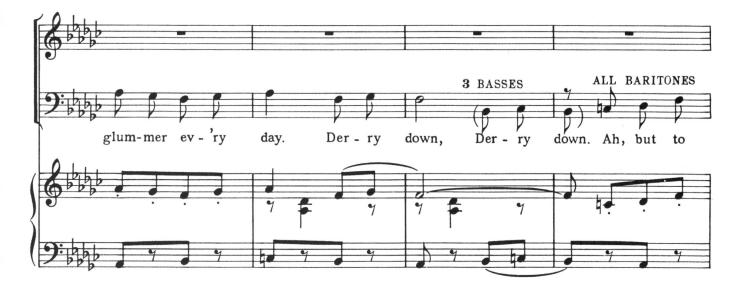

glum-mer ev-'ry day. Der-ry down, Der-ry down. Ah, but to

3 BASSES   ALL BARITONES

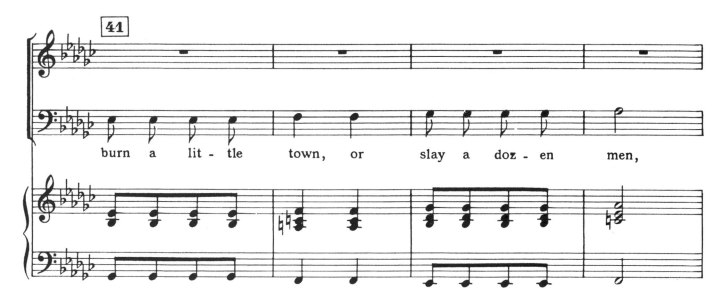

burn a lit-tle town, or slay a doz-en men,

Chappell

Chappell

night I be-head-ed a man who was beat-ing his na-ked wife. _____

add TENORS

ALL:

Lol-ly Lo! _____ Lol-ly

BASSES & BARITONES

Lol-ly Lo! _____ Lol-ly

SIR DINADAN: 77 F

Lo! _____ I can still hear his wid-ow

Lo! _____

Chappell

Fie on good-ness, Fie!

Fie on good-ness, Fie! Lech - 'ry and

93

TENORS: (shout)

ar - rest - ed

vice have been ar - rest - ed. Not a maid - en is

101 **H**
2 TENORS

Vir - gins can

ev - er-more in threat.

145

47520 Chappell

146

SOLO TENOR
(SCOTS KNIGHT)

OTHERS: Ny-ah

Fie! How we roar'd and brawn'd in Scot-land! Not a

Fie!

Ny-ah

law was e'er o - bey'd And when woo - in' called in

Ny-ah

Scot-land We'd grab an - y pass-ing maid. Ah, my heart is still in

Chappell

Chappell

148

47520

Chappell

Chappell

Chappell

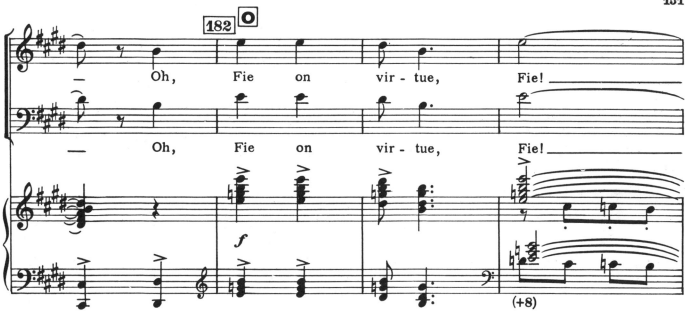

Oh, Fie on vir-tue, Fie!

Oh, Fie on vir-tue, Fie!

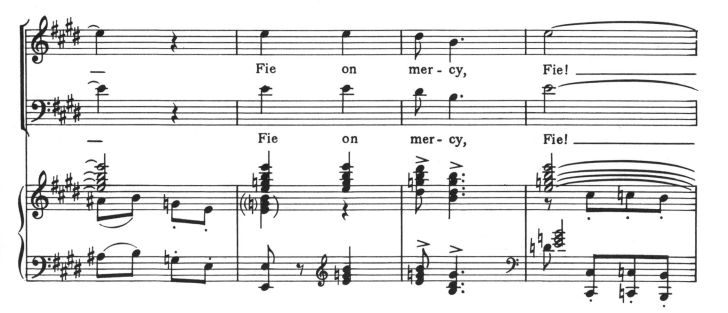

Fie on mer-cy, Fie!

Fie on mer-cy, Fie!

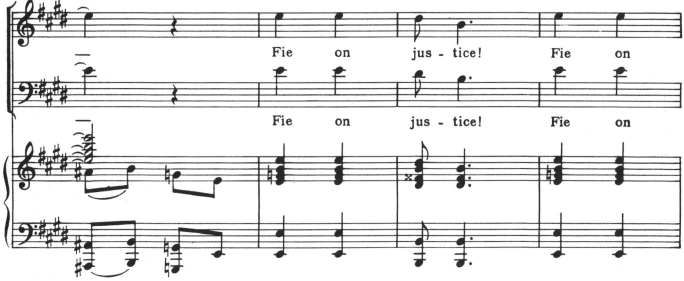

Fie on jus-tice! Fie on

Fie on jus-tice! Fie on

Chappell

Chappell

No.22 Guenevere's entrance and "If Ever I Would Leave You"

Chappell

If Ever I Would Leave You

Chappell

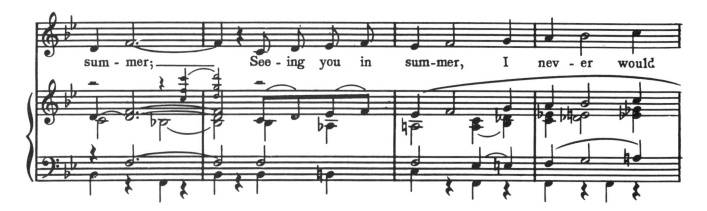

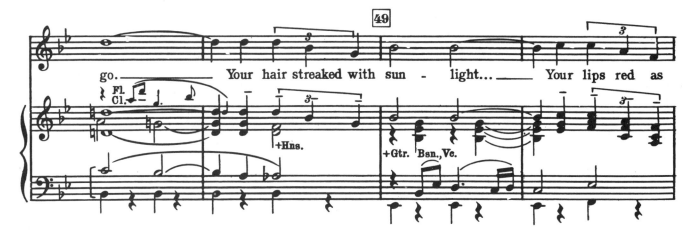

Chappell

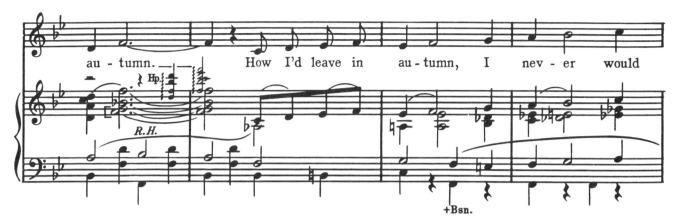

au - tumn. How I'd leave in au - tumn, I nev - er would

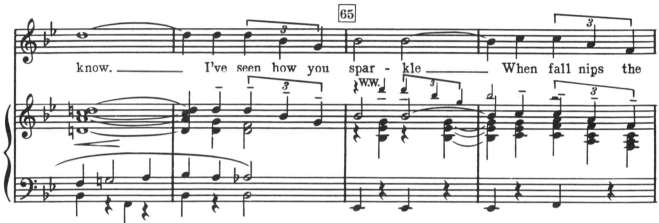

65

know. I've seen how you spar - kle When fall nips the

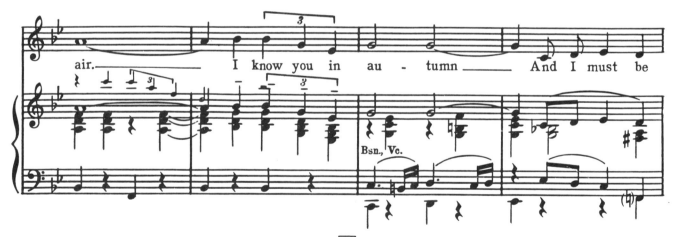

air. I know you in au - tumn And I must be

73

there. And could I leave you run - ning mer - ri - ly through the

Chappell

snow? _____ Or on a win-try eve-ning when you catch the fi-re's

81

glow? _____ If ev-er I would leave you, _____ How could it be in

spring-time, _____ Know-ing how in spring I'm be-witch'd by you

89

so? _____ Oh, no, not in spring-time! _____ Sum-mer, win-ter or

fall!

No, nev - er could I leave you _____ at

all. _____

(ENCORE) *passionato*

stringendo e cresc.

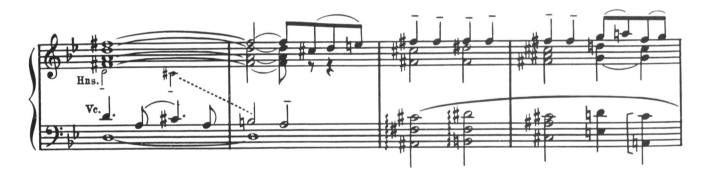

Hns.

Vc.

If ev - er I would leave you, _____ How could it be in

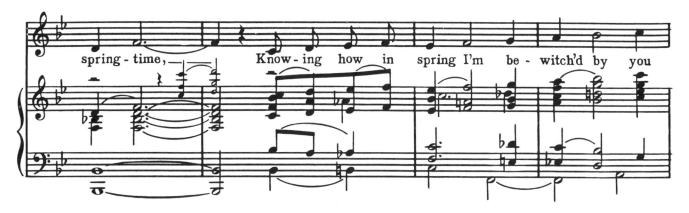

spring - time, Know - ing how in spring I'm be - witch'd by you

113

so? Oh, no, not in spring - time! Sum - mer, win - ter or

fall! No, nev - er could I leave you at

all.

(Dialogue)

Chappell

No. 23   The Seven Deadly Virtues

Cue: ARTHUR: The adage "blood is thicker than water", was invented by undeserving relatives. *(He exits)*
MORDRED: Virtue and proper deeds, Your Majesty, like what?

   Copyright © 1960 (unpub.) & 1962 by Alan Jay Lerner and Frederick Loewe

chaps, Who love a life of fail-ure and en - nui. Take

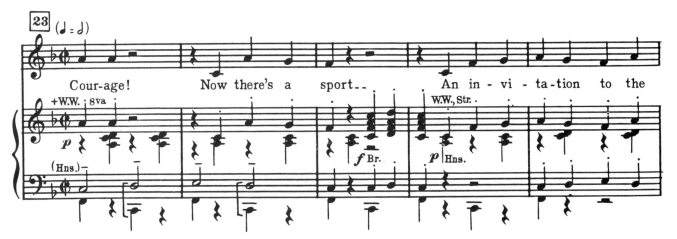

Cour-age! Now there's a sport... An in - vi - ta-tion to the

state of rig-or mort! And Pur - i - ty! A no-ble

yen! And ver - y rest-ful ev -'ry now and then.

Chappell

162

I find Hu - mil - i - ty means to be hurt; It's not the

earth the meek in - her - it, it's the dirt. Hon - es - ty is

fa - tal and should be ta - boo. Dil - i - gence? A fate I would

hate. If Char - i - ty means giv - ing, I give it to

47520

Chappell

Chappell

can - not wait to rush in Where an - gels fear to go. With

all those sev - en dead - ly vir - tues, Free and hap - py

lit - tle me has not been

cursed.

Chappell

No. 24

Change Of Scene

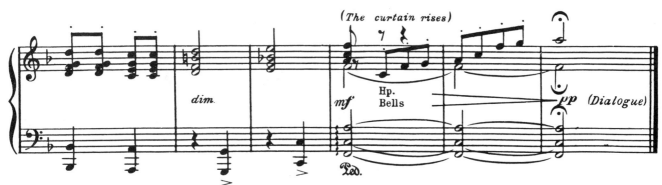

No. 25   # What Do The Simple Folk Do?

Cue: GUENEVERE: Royalty never can. Why is that, Arthur? Other people do. They seem to have ways and means of finding respite. What do they do? Farmers, cooks, blacksmiths.....

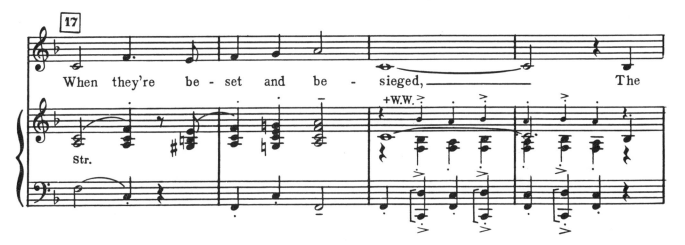

When they're be-set and be-sieged, _____ The

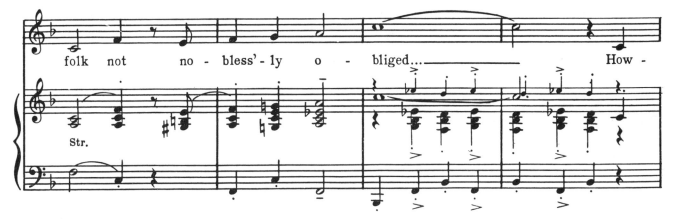

folk not no-bless'-ly o - bliged... _____ How -

ev - er do they man-age To shed their wea - ry lot? Oh,

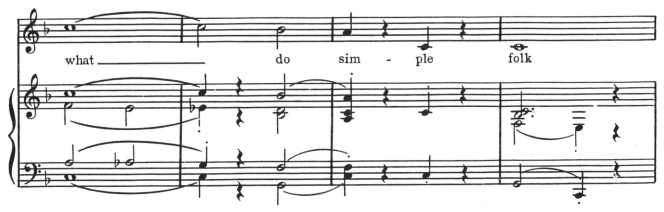

what _____ do sim - ple folk

Chappell

do _____ We do not? _____

+Bsn., Hns.

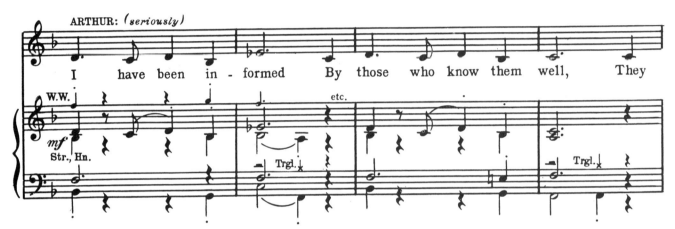

ARTHUR: *(seriously)*

I have been in - formed By those who know them well, They

W.W.

mf

Str., Hn.

etc.

Trgl.

Trgl.

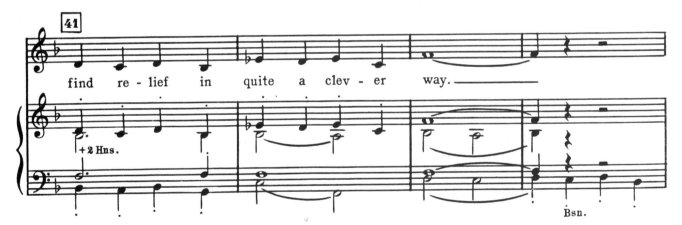

find re - lief in quite a clev - er way. _____

+ 2 Hns.

Bsn.

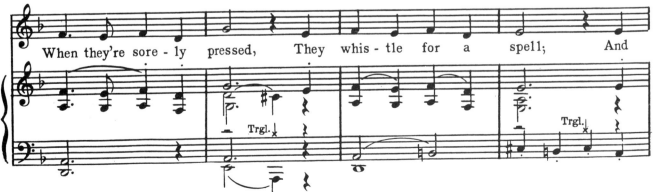

When they're sore - ly pressed, They whis - tle for a spell; And

Trgl.

Trgl.

Chappell

169

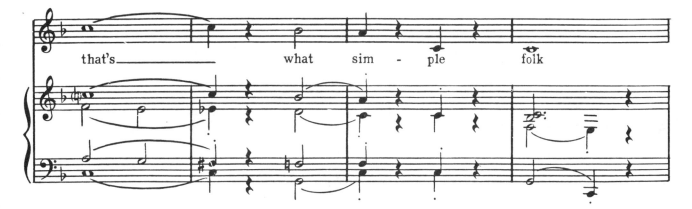

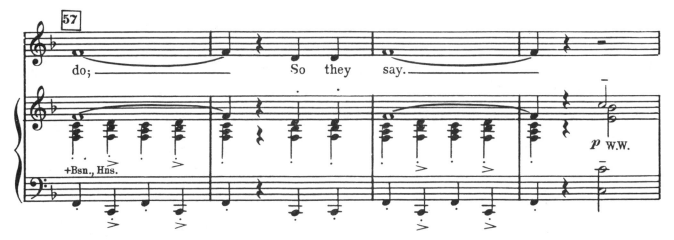

47520

Chappell

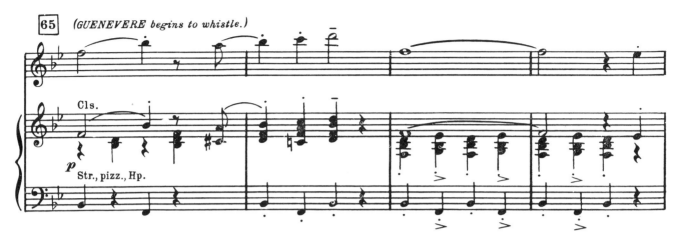

65 *(GUENEVERE begins to whistle.)*

Cls.

p Str., pizz., Hp.

(ARTHUR joins in)

73

Gtr., Str. arco

(GUENEVERE suddenly stops, thinks for a moment, then turns to him.)

GUENEVERE:

What

dim.

pp

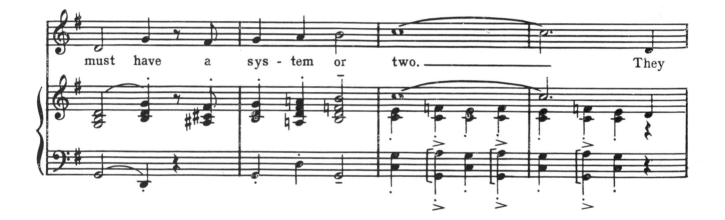

tricks a roy-al high-ness Is min-us From birth. Bells

What then, I won-der do they _____ To

chase all the gob-lins a - way?_____ They

have some tri-bal sorc'-ry You have-n't men-tioned yet. Oh,

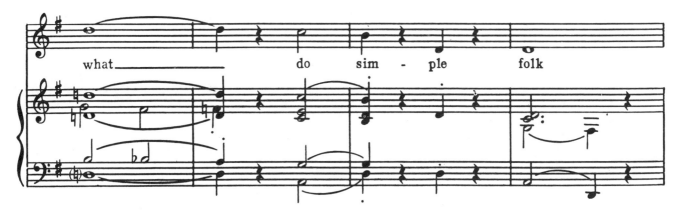

what_____ do sim - ple folk

193

do _____ To for - get?_____

ARTHUR:

Of - ten I am told They dance a fier-y dance, And

201

whirl til they're com-plete-ly un - cen - trolled._____

Soon the mind is blank, And all are in a trance, A

209

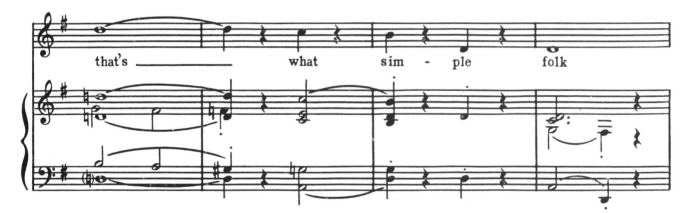

vi'-lent trance a-stound-ing to be-hold._____ And

that's_____ what sim - ple folk

217

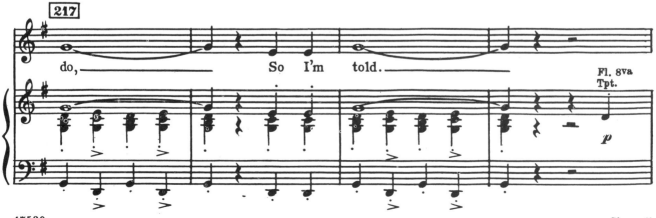

do,_____ So I'm told._____

Chappell

(ARTHUR invites GUENEVERE to dance.)

Bsn., Hns.

f

Tutti

(They dance a wild hornpipe.)

225 Poco più mosso

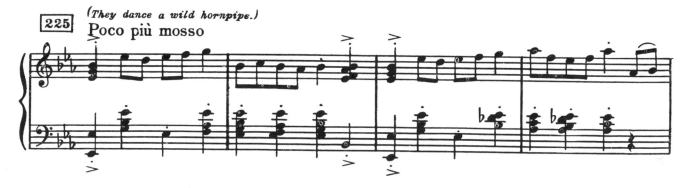

sfz *sfz* *sfz*

233

f sempre

sfz *sfz* *sfz*

Chappell

Chappell

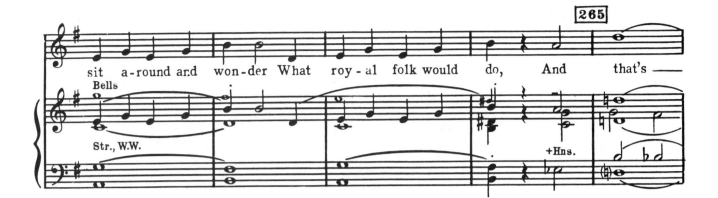

sit a-round and won-der What roy-al folk would do, And that's —

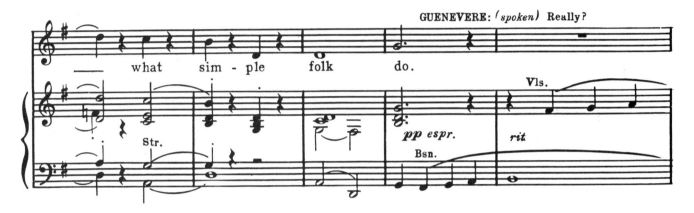

— what sim-ple folk do.

GUENEVERE: *(spoken)* Really?

ARTHUR: I have it on the best authority. BOTH:

273 **Poco meno mosso**

Yes, that's ___ what sim-ple

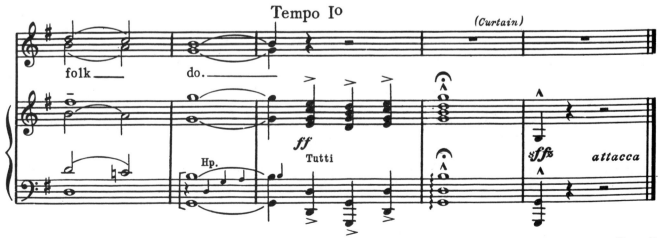

Tempo Iº

(Curtain)

folk ___ do. ___

Chappell

The Enchanted Forest

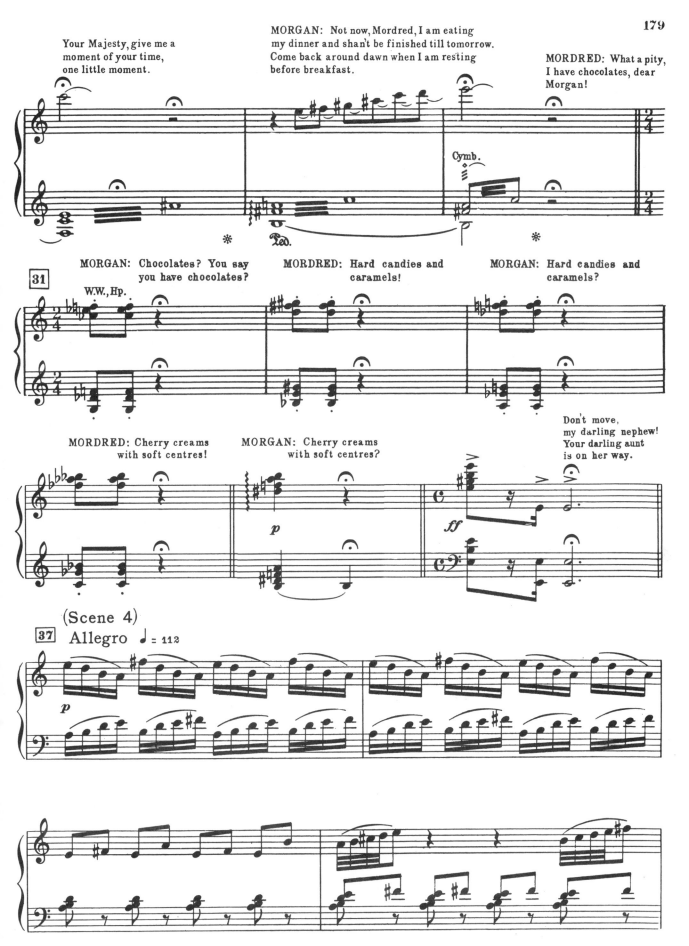

Chappell

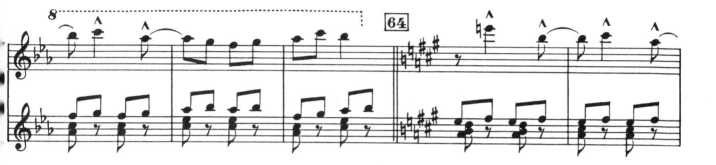

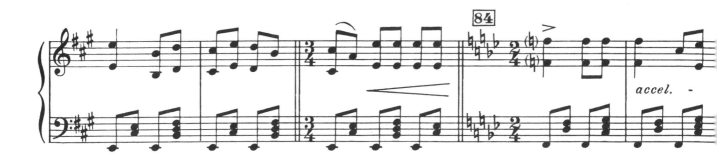

No. 27

The Persuasion

Cue: MORGAN LE FEY: How do you know I build invisible walls?
MORDRED: Mummy told me. Please, dear aunt?
MORGAN: No, I will not harm little Wart. Court!

Copyright © 1961 (unpub.) & 1962 by Alan Jay Lerner and Frederick Loewe   Chappell

Fresh mar - zi - pan!

All yours it will be If you

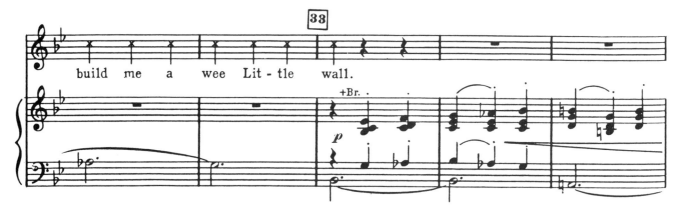

build me a wee Lit - tle wall.

MORGAN:

No,

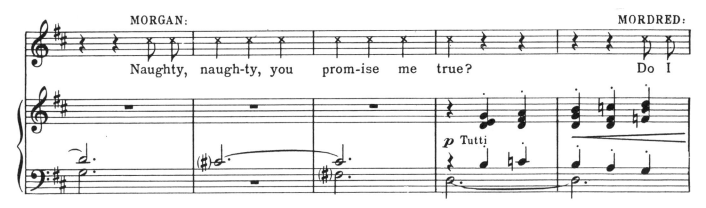

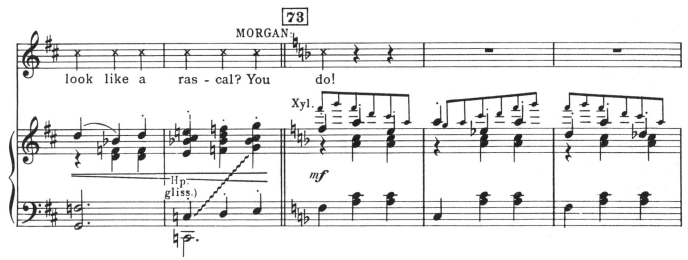

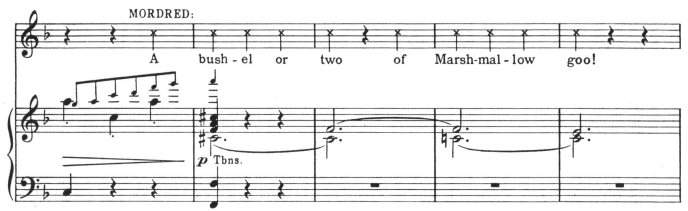

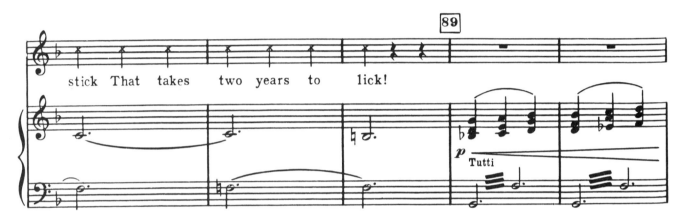

Chappell

105

hur - ry and mix Some in - vis - i - ble bricks.

f W.W., Br.

MORDRED:

Oh, Queen, you're a joy!

MORGAN:

MORDRED leaves.

MORGAN hides behind a tree.

Be - gone, nas - ty boy!

+Str.

ff Tutti

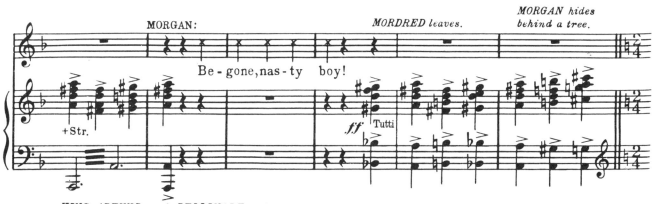

KING ARTHUR and PELLINORE enter.

117 Allegro

PELLINORE: Where's the bird, Arthur?

121

8va

f W.W., Hp. Str.

Tpt. *dim.*

Br.

Where's the bird? You hit it. I saw it. Where did it go?

125

ARTHUR: Strange, Pelly, I've never seen this forest before. I used to play in this valley, when I was a boy. But it was like a meadow. There were no trees.
PELLINORE: Nature, old boy. Things pop up, you know.

8va

p

Str., Bell

pp misterioso

Chappell

ARTHUR: Sh-h-h. It's awfully quiet around here, isn't it? *(MORGAN appears and listens)* Not a leaf rustling, not a whisper in the woods..... It makes one feel rather drowsy. Would you care to rest a bit?

PELLINORE: No thank you, old man. I want to find that bird, what? I mean, if you hit a bird with an arrow, it ought to fall down like a gentleman. Unless it's a lady bird *(Exit)*

ARTHUR: Merlyn, do you remember how often we walked in this valley when I was a boy?

Do you know what I miss of those days? Not my youth. My innocence. My innocence. *(He closes his eyes)*

No. 28   The Invisible Wall

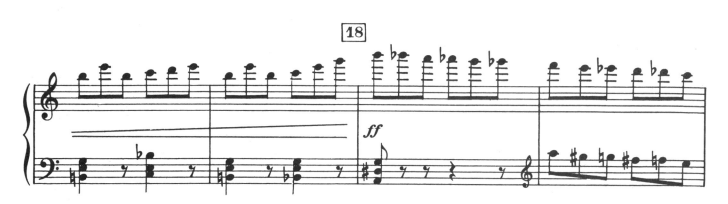

Chappell

Chappell

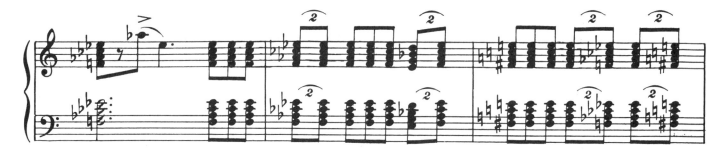

Chappell

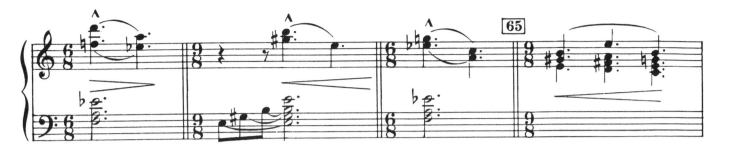

47520

Chappell

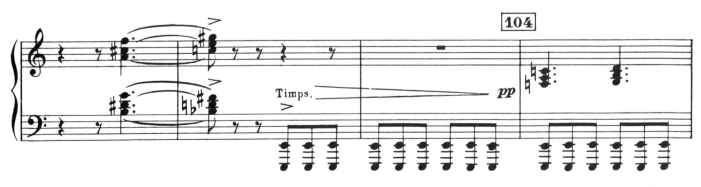

Chappell

No. 29 — Change Of Scene

Cue: ARTHUR:... Find Lance. Find Jenny. Tell them to be careful.
PELLINORE: You know, Arthur?
ARTHUR: Do as I say, Pelly! *(PELLINORE exits)* Morgan Le Fey!

Chappell

No.30 Change Of Scene And Incidental Music

Cue: MORDRED: Pellinore, in a little while, I shall be in charge of this Castle. And shortly after that, gentlemen, the Kingdom.

(Curtain)

Passionato in 2

Piano

Tutti *ff*

(The Curtain rises)

Fl. Ob. Vlns. Hns. Hns. Vc.

63 Adagio

LANCELOT: *(speaks)* Jenny, I was in the garden, I couldn't sleep, I saw the light in your window

p

I knew you were alone I tried to stay away, I tried, *(They embrace)*

GUENEVERE: Did anyone see you?

LANCELOT: No one, Jenny

72

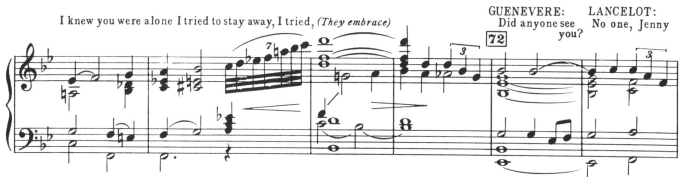

GUENEVERE: LANCELOT:
Don't be afraid But I am afraid. I swear we're alone, There's nothing to fear. Arthur won't be back until

Dialogue continues

Chappell

No. 31 If Ever I Would Leave You (Reprise)

Cue: LANCELOT: Forgive me Jenny... *etc.*

Chappell

Sum-mer, win-ter or fall. _____ No ne-ver could I

leave you _____ at all. _____

Dialogue

No. 32   Menacing Scream (Prior to Guenevere)

Cue: LANCELOT: ... Someone will come.

This discordant trill comes as Lancelot grabs Mordred and covers the scuffle.
Then segue GUENEVERE No.33

Piano

Segue

Chappell

No. 33

Guenevere

Copyright © 1960 (unpub.) & 1962 by Alan Jay Lerner and Frederick Loewe

Chappell

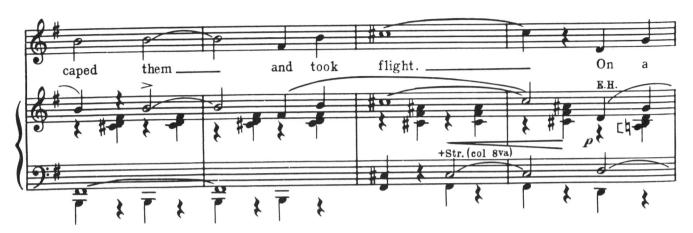

sen - tenced _____ to the flame. _____ As the

Fl.,Bs.Cl.,Bsn.

Tbns.

p

37

dawn _____ filled the sky, _____ On the

Hns.,Str.,Gtr.

Tbns.

day _____ she would die, _____ There was

45

won - der _____ far and near: _____ Would the

Chappell

Chappell

Chappell

Lyrics:

And the mo - ment _____ now was here _____

And the mo - ment _____ now was here _____

For the end of _____ Gue - ne - vere. _____

For the end of _____ Gue - ne - vere. _____

GUENEVERE enters. She is accompanied by a

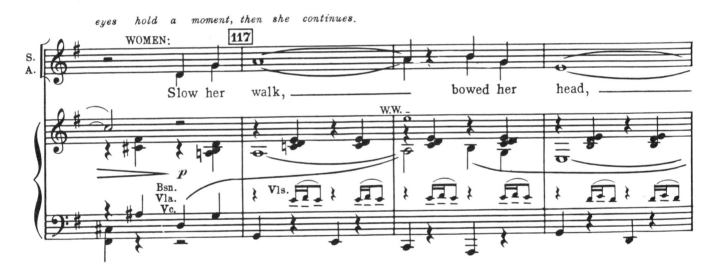

Chappell

Chappell

And lo! A - head the ar - my, hold-ing a -loft his spear, Came

ARTHUR: Lance!

Lance - lot to save his dear Gue - ne - vere. _____

165 Lance! Come save her. HERALD: Shall I signal the torch, Your Majesty? DINADAN: *(rushing*

in) Arthur, we're being attacked Lancelot leads an army from France, They're storming the gate

173

Shall I double the guard?
Arthur, you're inviting a massacre! *(He rushes off)* ARTHUR: Save her, Lance, save her!

Chappell

By the score _____ fell the dead, _____

By the score _____ fell the dead, _____

As the yard _____ turned to red. _____

As the yard _____ turned to red. _____

Count-less num - bers _____ felt his spear, _____

Count-less num - bers _____ felt his spear, _____

Chappell

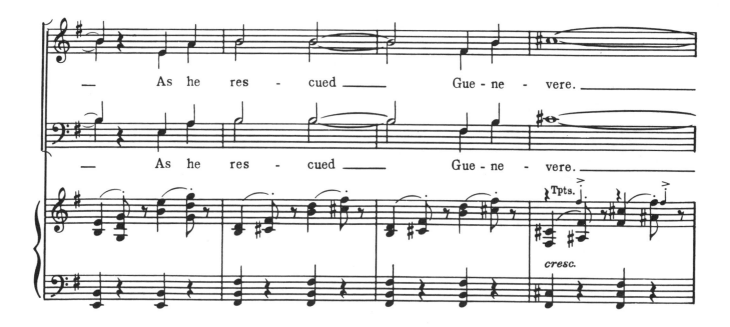

As he res - cued _____ Gue - ne - vere. _____

As he res - cued _____ Gue - ne - vere. _____

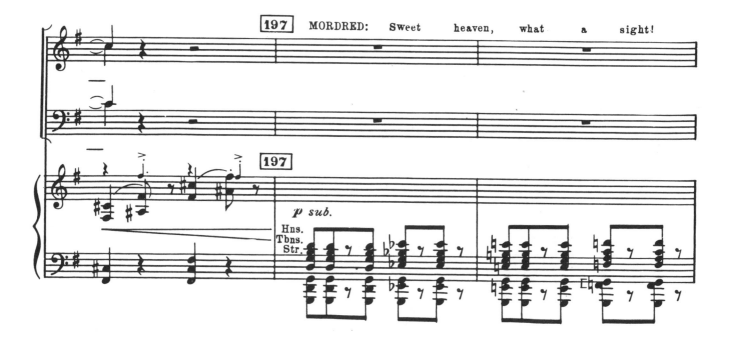

197 MORDRED: Sweet heaven, what a sight!

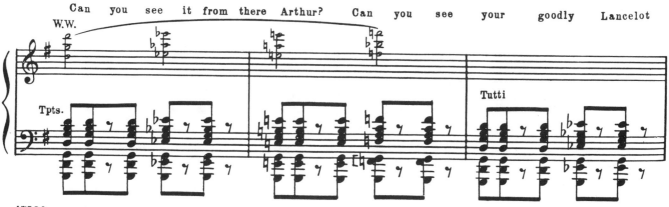

Can you see it from there Arthur? Can you see your goodly Lancelot murdering your goodly knights? Your table is cracking, Arthur.

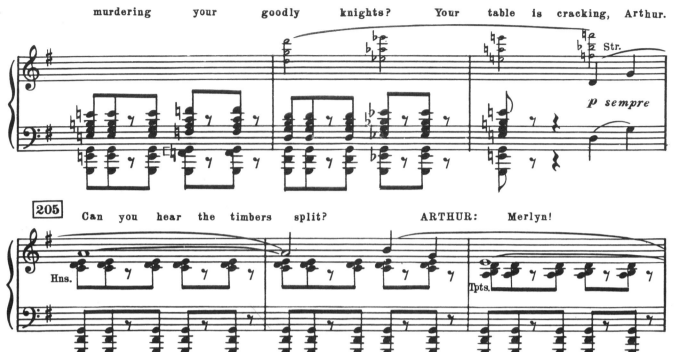

205 Can you hear the timbers split? ARTHUR: Merlyn!

Merlyn, make me a hawk. Let me fly away from here.

MORDRED: What a failure you are, **213** Arthur!

How did you think you could survive without

Chappell

Chappell

In the dy - ing ____ can - dle's gleam ____

In the dy - ing ____ can - dle's gleam ____

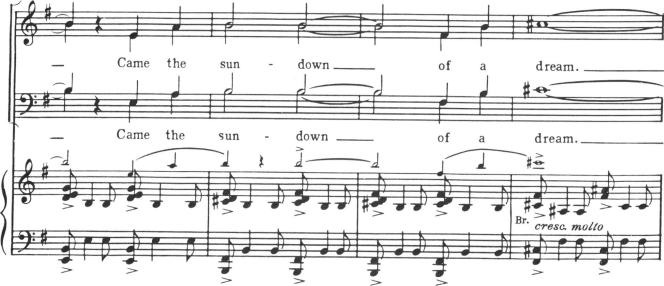

Came the sun - down ____ of a dream. ____

Came the sun - down ____ of a dream. ____

CLARIUS: (*entering*) Arthur, over 80 Knights slain! Lancelot and his Frenchman head for the Channel and

Chappell

home. Arthur, we want revenge!   You must lead us to France   *(He exits)*

ARTHUR: Oh God, is it all to start again?   Is my

245 almighty fling at peace to be over so

soon?   Am   I   back   where   I   began?

Am I?   Am I?   *f*   253

S.
A.
Gue - ne - vere, _____   Gue - ne -

T.
B.
Gue - ne - vere, _____   Gue - ne -

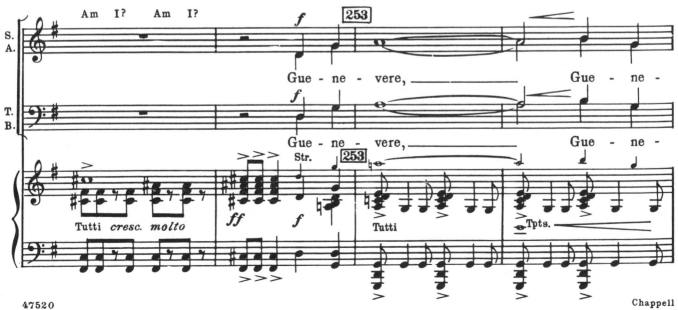

Tutti *cresc. molto*   *ff* *f*   Tutti

216

(Men enter with the King's armour

vere! _____ In that dim, _____ mourn - ful

year, _____ Saw the men she _____ held most

dear _____ Go to war for _____ Gue - ne -

and sword. The armour is put on him.) 261

etc.

47520

Chappell

dear _____ Go to war for _____ Gue - ne -

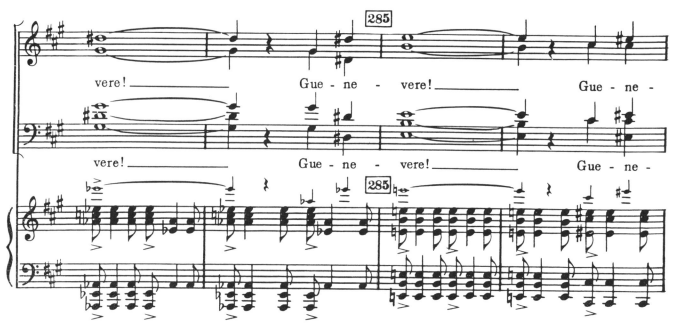

vere! _____ Gue - ne - vere! _____ Gue - ne -

vere! _____ Gue - ne - vere!

293

(All but ARTHUR leave as the SCENE CHANGES to the battlefield

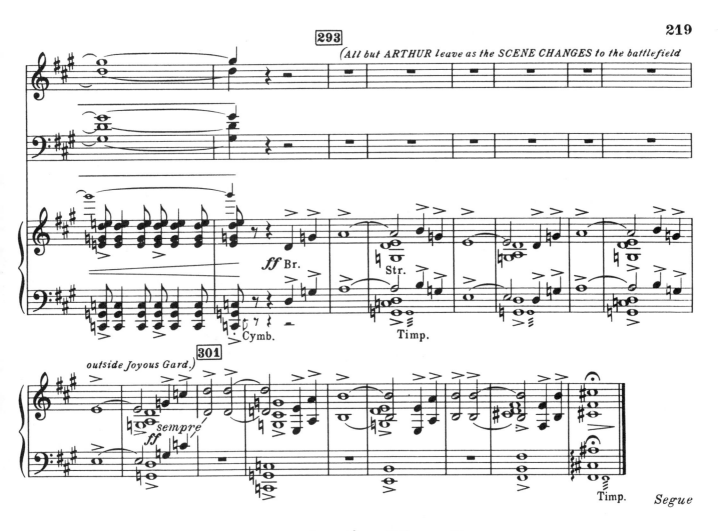

ff Br.
Cymb.
Str.
Timp.

outside Joyous Gard.)

301

sempre ff

Timp.

Segue

No. 34 Lancelot's Fanfare
(Opening of Scene 8)

On ENTRANCE of French Knights and Lancelot's Standard Bearer

Bright tempo ♩ = 96

Muted Tpts.

Piano

ff

At cue

ARTHUR: reality or memory

Tpt.(distant)

Dialogue   *Dialogue*

47520

Chappell

No. 35 Farewell (Melos)

Cue: GUENEVERE: ..."I still love you, Arthur."

Andante

Piano

pp (under dialogue)

GUENEVERE and
SISTERS exit.
ARTHUR (left alone)

"My dearest Love."

Dialogue

Chappell

No. 36   Finale Ultimo

Cue: ARTHUR: And for as long as you live you will remember what I, the King, tell you; and you will do as I command.
TOM: Yes, my King

Allegro moderato

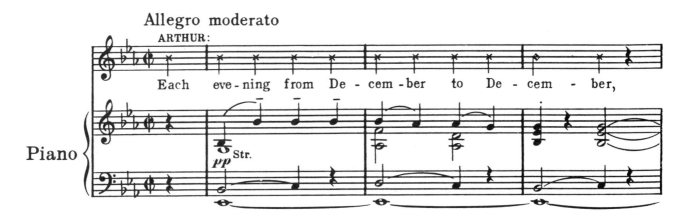

ARTHUR:

Each eve - ning from De - cem - ber to De - cem - ber,

Be - fore you drift to sleep up - on your cot,

⑨

Think back on all the tales that you re - mem - ber

Of Ca - me - lot.

Chappell

Ask ev'-ry per-son if he's heard the sto - ry,——

And tell it strong and clear if he has not:

That once there was a fleet-ing wisp of glo - ry——

Called Ca - me - lot.

Chappell

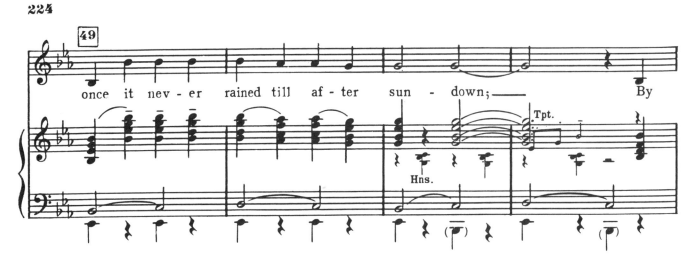

once it nev-er rained till af-ter sun - down; _____ By

eight a. m. the morn-ing fog had flown. _____ Don't

let it be for-got That once there was a spot For one brief shin-ing

mo-ment that was known As Ca - me -

Chappell

My teacher Merlyn, who always remembered things that haven't happened

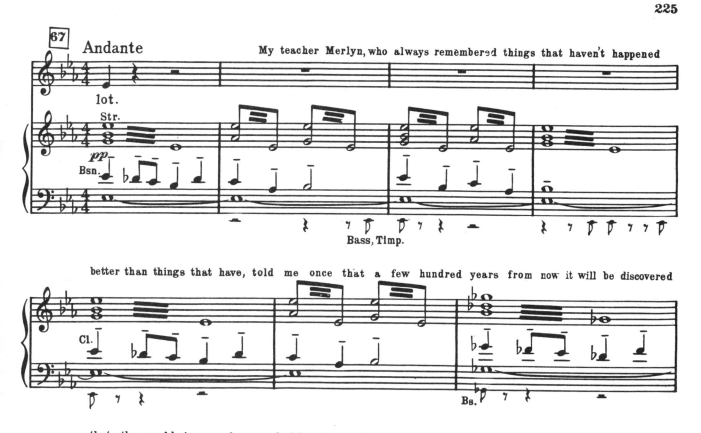

better than things that have, told me once that a few hundred years from now it will be discovered

that the world is round... round like the table at which we sat with such high hope and

noble purpose. If you do what I ask, perhaps people will remember how we of

Camelot went questing for right and honour and justice. Perhaps one day men will sit around

Chappell

this world as we did once at our table and go questing once more... for right... honour.. and justice.

PELLINORE: *(enters carrying Excalibur)* Arthur...?

Tempo I⁰

(From a distance) ARTHUR: Give me the sword.

CHORUS: Ca - me - lot!

Ca - me - lot!

PELLINORE: Here.

ARTHUR: Kneel, Tom, kneel.

With this sword,

Ca - me - lot!

Ca - me - lot!

Chappell

227

47520

Chappell

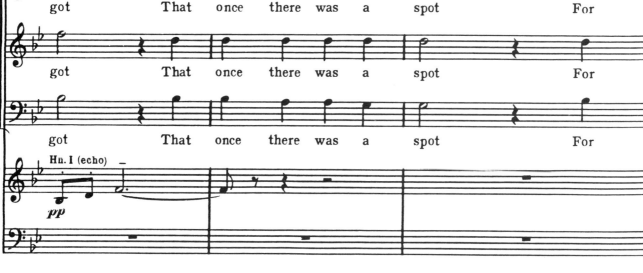

You'll see, Pelly. Now, run, Sir Tom! Behind the lines.   TOM: Yes, Milord. *(He runs off)*

got   That   once   there   was   a   spot   For

got   That   once   there   was   a   spot   For

got   That   once   there   was   a   spot   For

got   That   once   there   was   a   spot   For

Hn. I (echo)

pp

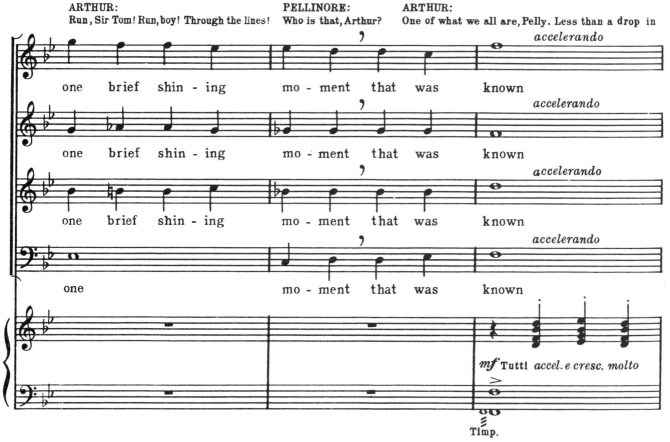

ARTHUR:
Run, Sir Tom! Run, boy! Through the lines!   PELLINORE: Who is that, Arthur?   ARTHUR: One of what we all are, Pelly. Less than a drop in

accelerando

one   brief   shin - ing   mo - ment   that   was   known

accelerando

one   brief   shin - ing   mo - ment   that   was   known

accelerando

one   brief   shin - ing   mo - ment   that   was   known

accelerando

one   mo - ment   that   was   known

mf Tutti *accel. e cresc. molto*

Timp.

the great blue motion of the sunlit sea. But it seems some of the drops sparkle, Pelly.   Some of them do sparkle!

Chappell

No. 37 Music For Curtain Calls And Exit

Chappell

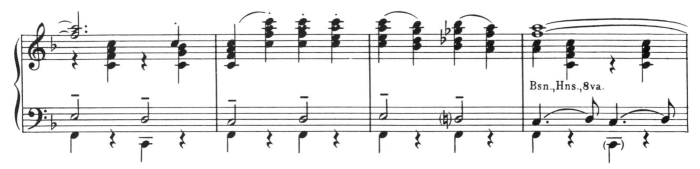

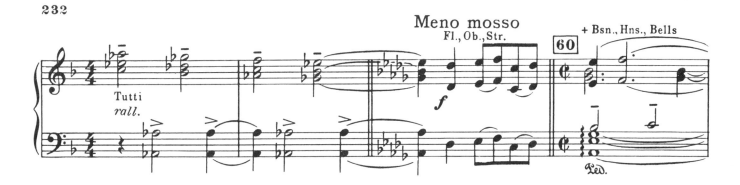

Chappell

Chappell

Chappell

Printed in Great Britain by The Panda Group, Suffolk CB9 8PR · 09/99

Chappell